Chemistry and Therapy
of
Chronic Cardiovascular Disease

Publication Number 438
AMERICAN LECTURE SERIES®

A Monograph in

The BANNERSTONE DIVISION *of*
AMERICAN LECTURES IN LIVING CHEMISTRY

Edited by

I. NEWTON KUGELMASS, M.D., Ph.D., Sc.D.
Consultant to the Departments of Health and Hospitals
New York City

Chemistry and Therapy of Chronic Cardiovascular Disease

By

RICHARD J. JONES, A.B., M.A., M.D.

Associate Professor, Department of Medicine
University of Chicago

and

LOUIS COHEN, B.S., M.D.

Instructor, Department of Medicine
University of Chicago
Advanced Research Fellow
American Heart Association

CHARLES C THOMAS · PUBLISHER
Springfield · Illinois · U.S.A.

CHARLES C THOMAS • PUBLISHER
BANNERSTONE HOUSE
301-327 East Lawrence Avenue, Springfield, Illinois, U.S.A.

© 1961, by CHARLES C THOMAS • PUBLISHER

Library of Congress Catalog Card Number: 60-15851

With THOMAS BOOKS careful attention is given to all details of manufac-
turing and design. It is the Publisher's desire to present books that are satisfactory as to their physical qualities and artistic possibilities and appropriate for
their particular use. THOMAS BOOKS will be true to those laws of quality
that assure a good name and good will.

Printed in the United States of America

To our wives and children

FOREWORD

Our Living Chemistry Series was conceived by Editor and Publisher to advance the newer knowledge of chemical medicine in the cause of clinical practice. The interdependence of chemistry and medicine is so great that physicians are turning to chemistry, and chemists to medicine in order to understand the underlying basis of life processes in health and disease. Once chemical truths, proofs and convictions become sound foundations for clinical phenomena, key hybrid investigators clarify the bewildering panorama of biochemical progress for application in everyday practice, stimulation of experimental research and extension of postgraduate instruction. Each of our monographs thus unravels the chemical mechanisms and clinical management of many diseases that have remained relatively static in the minds of medical men for three thousand years. Our new Series is charged with the *nisus élan* of chemical wisdom, supreme in choice of international authors, optimal in standards of chemical scholarship, provocative in imagination for experimental research, comprehensive in discussions of scientific medicine, and authoritative in chemical perspectives of human disorders.

Dr. Jones and Dr. Cohen of Chicago reveal approved methods of clinical control and timely prevention of chronic cardiovascular disease in terms of chemical mechanisms evolved in this era. The clinical thesis is built upon the scientific foundations laid by Caesalpine and Harvey in blood circulation, Hales and Porter in hemodynamics, Hope and Starling in heart failure, Bright and Goldblatt in hypertension, and Marie and Herrick in myocardial infarction. The chemical amplifications are based on underlying mechanisms of degenerative decrements in form and function rather than on pathological changes that reflect the final breakdown of the body's capacity to cope with biological transactions. Nature abhors ageing; degeneration seems the only disease, and all others run into this one. But the authors' integrated interpretation of the mechanism and management of the chronic diseases of cardiovascular origin gives us a better understanding of those difficult years in the "last of life for which the first was made." Human existence is thus being maintained with diminishing degeneration by optimal nutrition for optimal health for optimal longevity, not only to add years to life but life to years. Nevertheless, the cardiovascular system remains the weakest strand in the thread of life and cardiovascular disease, the greatest threat to disability and death.

I. Newton Kugelmass, M.D., Ph.D., Sc.D., *Editor*

PREFACE

OUR AGING POPULATION PROVIDES a great challenge to medicine as well as to our social and governmental institutions. At the same time that the birth rate has reached a new high level, the death rate per capita has achieved a new low level by virtue of both a reduction in infant mortality and in deaths due to infectious agents. This has led to a relative and absolute increase in the rates of morbidity and mortality due to cardiovascular diseases (in 1957: 500 deaths per 100,000 population, or fifty-two percent of deaths from all causes). Consequently, a break-through in the control of cardiovascular diseases will, more than anything else, make a change in our national mortality rate. This is not as unlikely a prospect as was once thought; for arteriosclerosis, especially atherosclerosis, is now felt to be a perhaps reversible disease not necessarily related to age. Furthermore, of these cardiovascular deaths approximately thirty percent are attributable to thrombotic disease, against which anticoagulant therapy has recently had favorable influence. While great strides are being made each year in the understanding and control of still other cardiovascular diseases, the new knowledge and better management of the diseases discussed here is due in large measure to basic advances in biochemistry and pharmacology.

Whereas the great clinicians of a generation ago were likely to be specially trained in pathology, and most eminent clinicians of today underwent basic training in physiology, it will become obvious from the present vantage point that the present students of medicine must order their training with a heavy accent on chemistry. This has become as true for the pathologist and the other preclinical scientists as the clinician.

The present monograph emphasizes the position of chemistry in understanding the more recent advances in certain chronic cardiovascular diseases; this discipline unlocks new information concerning the mechanisms of disease and provides us with new therapeutic agents and insight as to their use. It is not intended to be a complete discussion of the pathogenesis or therapy of all chronic cardiovascular diseases but only of atherosclerosis and the often recurrent complications of thrombosis and congestive heart failure which are common to all types of chronic cardiovascular disease. Atherosclerosis, while a disease unto itself, may also be looked upon as a frequent complication in other types of heart disease. In the present state of our knowledge, the treatment of chronic cardiovascular disease must often be directed against these very complications. It is chemistry more than any other discipline that will provide the understanding ultimately necessary not only to treat these disorders but also to prevent their cause.

The major topics as presented follow the historical development of knowledge in the management of chronic cardiovascular disease: the only specific therapy until World War II was the treatment of congestive heart failure; more recently long-term anticoagulant therapy has proven to be prophylactic; and now the possibility of atherosclerosis prevention is under intensive investigation. It is the chemical bases for the pathogenesis and therapy of congestive heart failure, thromboembolism and atherosclerosis, which are examined here. Therapeutic agents used in other chronic cardiovascular disease might have been included under the present title but are excluded by considerations of space.

As one reviews the four sections of this monograph, the contrast will be apparent between our knowledge concerning the treatment of congestive heart failure, where applicable knowledge has been accumulating and seasoning for almost 200 years, and that surrounding the modern treatment of hypercholesteremia, where the indications for treatment and measures of success are still in controversy. Intermediate in clarity is our view of anticoagulants, which have been in use for only twenty years.

Much of the work that is presented here has derived from lectures given by the senior author for the American College of Physicians. The remainder involves a review of the pertinent literature leavened by our own clinical and laboratory experiences in the University of Chicago Clinics over the past ten years. Reference is made, insofar as possible, to material published before 1960.

ACKNOWLEDGMENTS

THE ORIGINAL WORK PRESENTED here was supported by a grant from The USPHS (H-1119) and grants from the Chicago and American Heart Associations. The personal work reported in this monograph which required the use of constant diets in hospitalized subjects was made possible by an institutional grant to the Argonne Cancer Research Hospital, USAEC, The University of Chicago. For the calculation and preparations of the diets in these experiments we are indebted to Miss Hogan and assistant dieticians of that hospital.

The authors are deeply indebted to Miss Lilian Roberts for her painstaking preparation of the manuscript, to Drs. Emmet B. Bay, Robert W. Wissler, Theodore Pullman and George Okita for their comments on certain portions of the manuscript; and to Dr. Lyle Van Ness, and especially Dr. Paul Kuhn, both assisted by Mrs. Barbara Helmstetter, for the collation of the results of anticoagulant therapy.

R. J. J.
L. C.

CONTENTS

	Page
Foreword	vii
Preface	ix
Acknowledgments	xi

SECTION I
CONGESTIVE HEART FAILURE

Chapter

I. INTRODUCTION	5
II. DIGITALIS	7
Chemistry of Digitalis	7
Clinical Effects of the Purified Glycosides	15
Metabolic Studies	18
III. ORAL DIURETICS	21
Carbonic Anhydrase Inhibition	23
Chlorothiazide	25
IV. SERUM ELECTROLYTES AND HEART FAILURE	31
Conclusion	33
References	33

SECTION II
THROMBOSIS

I. THROMBOSIS	41
The Pathogenesis of Thrombosis	42
II. BLOOD COAGULATION AND HEMOSTASIS	46
The Three Stages of Blood Coagulation	46
Lipids and Coagulation	52
Hemostasis	55

Chapter   *Page*

III. ANTICOAGULANTS 59

    Coumarin and Indanedione Anticoagulants 59

    Heparin 65

IV. THROMBOLYSIS 70

    Plasminogen 70

    Plasmin 72

    Diet 74

    Therapeutic Application 74

 V. ANTICOAGULANT THERAPY FOR MYOCARDIAL INFARCTION 76

    Thrombotic Complications and the Acute Infarct 76

    Long Term Anticoagulant Therapy:

        Prevention of Reinfarction 77

    References 83

SECTION III
ATHEROSCLEROSIS

 I. THE ATHEROSCLEROTIC PLAQUE 101

    Role of the Atheromatous Plaque in Coronary Occlusion .. 103

    Theories of Atheroma Formation 104

    The Chemistry of the Atheromatous Plaque 108

 II. THE SERUM LIPIDS 112

    The Chemistry of the Lipoproteins 115

III. BLOOD LIPIDS, PLAQUE, LIPIDS AND THE INFILTRATION THEORY . 121

    The Cooperative Study of Lipoproteins and Atherosclerosis 125

    References 129

SECTION IV
SERUM LIPID ALTERATIONS

 I. DIETARY 137

Chapter   Page

    Sterols 138
    Fat 140
    Carbohydrate 146
    Protein 147
    Total Calories 150

II. HUMORAL EFFECTS 152
    Estrogens 152
    Thyroid Hormones 154
    Heparin and the Clearing Factor 159
    "Stress" 165

III. THERAPEUTIC EFFORTS 168
    Fecal Sequestration of Alimentary Cholesterol 168
    Inhibition of Cholesterol Synthesis 175
    Miscellaneous Compounds 177
    Review of Therapy 178

References 180
Index 193

Chemistry and Therapy
of
Chronic Cardiovascular Disease

SECTION I
CONGESTIVE HEART FAILURE

Chapter I

INTRODUCTION

M YOCARDIAL INSUFFICIENCY, or congestive heart failure, is the commonest functional disorder of the heart and ultimately develops in more than half of all patients suffering from organic heart disease. The pathologic physiology of this condition is complicated and agreement on the exact sequence of events in such cases is not complete, but this symptom complex develops whenever the demand of the body tissues for oxygen is no longer met by the available cardiac output (1). Increased venous congestion, edema and cardiac dilatation may occur equally well at high levels of cardiac output as in hyperthyroid or beri-beri heart disease where the demand for oxygen and metabolites is increased, as at low levels of cardiac output, in rheumatic or coronary heart disease, where this demand is normal.

The most likely train of events stemming from a relative reduction in cardiac output is an increase in the end-diastolic pressure of the failing ventricle, which is transmitted backward to the venous system (either into the lungs or the periphery) producing a relative stasis of blood; this increased venous congestion leads to increased pressure, relative stagnation and consequent hypoxia at the venous capillary level which promote an increased transudation of plasma fluid through the capillary wall that is then augmented by the retention of salt and water by the kidney. In this initial reduction of cardiac output, with a laking of blood in the venous system, the circulation to vital organs is preserved at the expense of less critical organs, particularly the kidney. This results consistently in a decreased renal blood flow and an increased "filtration fraction," often in a decreased glomerular filtration rate, and sometimes in a "secondary aldosteronism." Which of these leads to the kidney's inability to excrete sodium has not been settled finally (2), but sodium retention does occur and water re-

5

tention is constantly associated with sodium retention by virtue of homeostatic devices which are still poorly defined.

The treatment of this condition must permit the heart the rest it needs by correcting any burdensome precipitating factors such as infection, anemia, thromboembolic phenomena, overactivity, valvular stenosis, and other factors which may be adding to the heart's work. In addition, treatment of the acute episode as well as prophylaxis against further misadventures may require no more than the improvement of myocardial efficiency and cardiac output by the use of a digitalis preparation. Sooner or later dietary sodium restriction may also be necessary; and should this become insufficient the complementary effect of various sodium diuretic (natriuretic) agents, such as carbonic anhydrase inhibitors, chlorothiazide, or mercurial diuretics will finally be required. All of these agents have dramatic effects upon the body chemistry, which must be taken into account; and, as congestive heart failure pursues its variable course, the point may ultimately be reached where the therapist directs the patient along an increasingly narrow path between relative cardiac compensation and a balance of serum and tissue electrolytes compatible with comfort and even life. It will be our purpose in the first chapters to summarize the chemistry of these agents and their effect on the body chemistry.

Chapter II

DIGITALIS

E<small>VER SINCE</small> W<small>ITHERING'S</small> discovery, digitalis preparations have been used with success to combat the symptoms of congestive heart failure. The dosage of the digitalis preparation must be individualized to the particular patient; it must "be continued until it acts either on the kidneys, the stomach, the pulse, or the bowels . . ." (3) and then a daily maintenance dose, estimated from previous experience with that "digitalizing" dose, is applied. More important than the unique effects of the particular preparation used by the physician is his own knowledge of and experience with that preparation. Nevertheless, recent advances in the isolation of new cardioactive glycosides and claims for their superiority require that we constantly take stock of our knowledge in the field of digitalis chemistry and pharmacology. The main emphasis here will be upon chemistry, for the physiological and clinical effects of digitalis have been well reviewed in three recent monographs (4, 5, 6.)

CHEMISTRY OF DIGITALIS

Glycoside Isolation: With the exception of strophanthin, the cardiac active drugs receiving clinical consideration today are all derived from the widely distributed *Digitalis purpurea* or from *Digitalis lanata* which is indigenous to the Balkan countries. The active principles of these plants, the glycosides, are extracted by ether from a watery mash of the leaves of the flowering plant, the yield being increased by 50% when 50% alcohol is used in the initial mash. The isolation of individual glycosides from such an extract was accomplished in the 1930's by Stoll and his co-workers (7, 8) who demonstrated the importance of limiting enzymatic deterioration of the initial extract by working in the dark, in vacuo, at low temperatures, and by increasing the salt content of the mash. The original technique involved repeated systematic partitions of the material between chloroform and aqueous methanol solutions. Although many glycosides have been isolated by this technique, newer glycosides are still being isolated by modern techniques of chromatography (9).

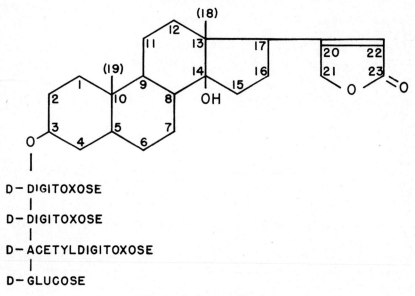

D – DIGITOXOSE
|
D – DIGITOXOSE
|
D – ACETYLDIGITOXOSE
|
D – GLUCOSE

Figure 1. Lanatoside A.

Lanatosides, A, B and C, as exemplified in Figure 1, were crystallized from *D. lanata;* two of these, A and B, were found to be identical to glycosides A and B from the *D. purpurea* extract, except that an extra acetyl group resided in the sugar chain. The purpurea glycosides are thus sometimes called deacetyl digilanids A and B. Lanatoside C has no counterpart in the purpurea derivatives, which, however, contain an amorphous glycoside fraction, gitalin, not found in *D. lanata.* Both lanatoside C and gitalin have recently been emphasized because of purported unique clinical advantages.

There are a host of other cardioactive glycosides, aside from strophanthins, which might be indicated in passing to illustrate their wide distribution in nature. These include the Scillaren A and B, periplocin and urginin derived from the oldest cardio-active substance known to man, the sea onion, or Squill; convallatoxin from Lily of the Valley; bufotoxin from the secretion of the parotid glands of toads; thevetin from the Malayan nut; and hellebrin from the Christmas Rose. Many other "new" glycosides are being found in the old crude extracts, as well, but, as with most of the above, they have not received clinical trial when, indeed, they have been isolated in large enough amounts to be identified.

Chemical Structure. The basic structure of the commonly used glycosides is a cyclopentenophenanthrene ring system, basic to all sterol and steroid compounds, which is hydroxylated at the C_3 and C_{14} positions, methylated at C_{10} and C_{13}, and to which an unsaturated lactone ring is attached at C_{17}. In the complete glycoside there is esterified, at the C_3 position, a sequence of two or three desoxy-sugars, i.e., sugars lacking one or two oxygen atoms, which terminates in a glucose molecule.

Only after taking special precautions to inhibit enzymatic hydrolysis did it become apparent that the so-called "purified glycosides" digitoxin and gitoxin were incomplete purpurea glycosides A and B, for a glucose molecule had been lost, and in the case of the lanatosides an acetyl group as well (7) (see Figure 2). The glycoside minus the entire string of sugars is called the aglycone or *genin,* and may be one of two types: *cardenolides* which contain the steroid nuclear structure attached to a 5-membered mono-unsaturated lactone ring: and *bufadienolides* which contain the same ring system attached to a 6-membered doubly unsaturated ring, as in Squill (10). Only the cardenolide derivatives illustrated in Figure 2 will concern us here.

The sugars associated with the glycosides discussed here are d-glucose, d-digitalose and d-digitoxose. Other cardioactive glycosides may contain one or more molecules of rhamnose, or such unique desoxyhexoses as 1- thevetose, d-gulomethylose, 1-oleandrose, d-sarmentose, d-digitinose and, in the strophanthins, d-cymarose (7). D-digitoxose and d-digitalose found in the digitalis glycosides have the following structural formulae respectively:

$$\begin{matrix} & \text{H H H} \\ & \text{H H O O O} \\ \text{O} = & \text{C-C-C-C-C-CH}_3 \\ & \text{H H H H} \end{matrix}$$

$$\begin{matrix} & \text{H} \quad\; \text{H} \\ & \text{H O H H O} \\ \text{O} = & \text{C-C-C-C-C-CH}_3 \\ & \text{H O O H} \\ & \text{C H} \\ & \text{H}_3 \end{matrix}$$

It is now generally agreed that the type or arrangement of sugars is important in determining cardiac activity, for these sugars affect the solubility and consequently the penetration of the active aglycone into the cell; the aglycone stripped of its sugar chain has virtually no cardiac activity because of its insolubility in water, and the replacement of one combination of desoxysugars in the sugar side chain by another may alter the glycoside's cardiotonic activity.

The cardenolides. Four of these and their related glycosides are depicted in Figure 2. Digitoxigenin is the simplest cardenolide with beta-hydroxyl groups at positions three and fourteen, and the 5-membered mono-unsaturated lactone ring attached in the

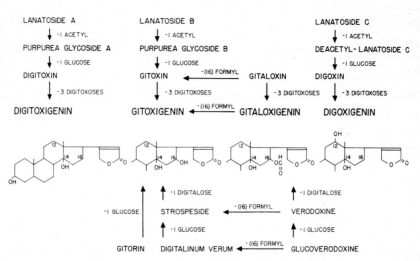

Figure 2. Relationships between the various glycosides and aglycones of digitalis. Digitoxigenin is a 3β, 14β-dihydroxy cardenolide; gitoxigenin is a 3β, 14β, 16β-trihydroxy cardenolide; gitaloxigenin is a 16 formyl-3β, 14β-dihydroxy cardenolide; and digoxigenin is a 3β, 12β, 14β-trihydroxy cardenolide. In these four aglycones the rings A and B are the same so that, except for digitoxigenin, they are not depicted. (Modified from Cloetens, DeMay, Dernier and Georges: Ref. 26).

beta position. Gitoxigenin and digoxigenin are isomers which contain a third beta-OH group at position twelve or sixteen. A fourth recently defined cardenolide is gitaloxigenin, a 16-formyl gitoxigenin. Recent chromatographic techniques have demonstrated many derivatives of these four basic cardenolides. As many as twenty-three different glycoside variations have been found in a simple alcoholic extract of Digitalis Purpurea, all ultimately hydrolyzable to one of the two aglycones digitoxigenin or gitoxigenin (12) ; some examples of these are seen in the lower half of Figure 2. Recent chromatographic studies suggest that, as Stoll suspected (8), amorphous gitalin contains not only digitoxin and gitoxin, but also two new glycosides, gitaloxin and strospeside. *Gitaloxin,* a 16-formyl gitoxin, is present in greater concentration and is more cardiotonic than *strospeside,* a gitoxigenin combined only with d-digitalose (13).

Stereoconfiguration. The unique position of the cardiac aglycones among the various cyclopentenophenanthrene chemicals of biological importance lies in their stereoconfiguration with regard to rings C and D (10, 11) : this is illustrated in Figure 3. All bile acids, sterols and steroids, except the cardioactive glycosides, have the B/C and C/D ring fusions of the *trans* variety, and in the natural or *allo* series of compounds, also have the A/B ring juncture of the *trans* variety. This means that their rings are joined in such a way that they tend to lie flat, their major surface each lying in the same plane, the hydrogen molecules at carbons 5, 9 and 14 fitting in the *alpha* position, i.e., on the opposite side of the ring from the two methyl groups at C_{10} and C_{13}. When the A/B ring juncture is of the *cis* variety, the hydrogen at C_5 falls into the beta position; this is illustrated in Figure 3 by the three dimensional view of 5-beta coprostanol (II) which is contrasted with 5-alpha cholestanol (I). The A/B and B/C junctures in the cardenolides are comparable to those of coprostanol (*cis-trans* formation), but present a C/D juncture of the *cis* configuration, with the C_{14} substituent in the alpha position. What this means in terms of the geometry of the rings of the steroid nucleus may be seen in Figure 3 (III) ; in the aglycones, the planes of rings A and D are virtually perpendicular to that of B and C!

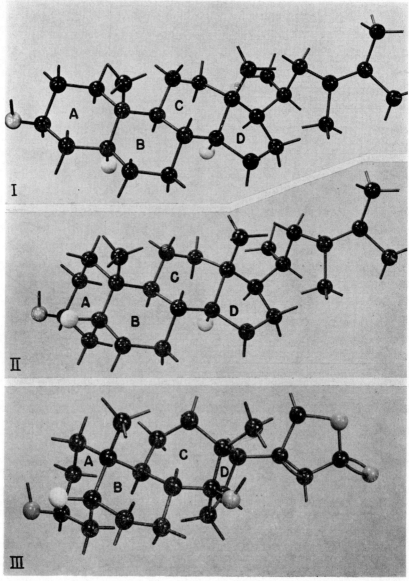

Figure 3. Photographed three dimensional models showing the different orientation of the cyclopentenophenanthrene rings A, B, C and D in: I. 5α-cholestan-3β-ol (dihydrocholesterol), II. 5β-coprostan-3β-ol (coprosterol) and III. 3β, 14β-dihydroxy cardenolide (digitoxigenin). Carbon molecules are represented by the black balls, oxygen by grey: hydrogen molecules are indicated by the open bonds except at C_5 and C_{14} where a white ball is seen: it

⟶

Another unique aspect of all cardioactive drugs is the *lactone ring*. All the digitalis and strophanthin derivatives contain the same 5-membered alpha, beta mono-unsaturated lactone ring. Scillaren from Squill, and a few more remote cardioactive compounds have been found to have a 6-membered lactone ring, but one of its two carbon unsaturations remains in the same alpha, beta location. Lactone rings of these configurations are essential for cardiotonic activity. Early attempts to synthesize cardiotonic aglycones with a lactone moiety containing beta, gamma - unsaturation were unsuccessful; furthermore, any rupture or replacement of the lactone ring, or saturation of its double bond leads to virtual inactivation of cardiotonic properties (7).

Polarity. The duration and intensity of action of a particular glycoside are undoubtedly the most important factors in its clinical use. It has been shown that the cardiac glycosides and particularly digitoxin are bound more or less firmly to the plasma proteins while in transport. Earlier, salt fractionation of plasma from digitoxin-treated animals suggested that this glycoside was exclusively bound by albumin, but more recent studies using zone electrophoresis suggest that it is not bound exclusively, if at all, by albumin (14). While similar concentrations of lanatoside C or strophanthin will cause cardiac arrest whether infused in Ringer's solution or in human blood, the concentration of digitoxin in plasma must be ten times greater than in Ringer's solution to produce the same incidence of cardiac arrest. Lanatoside B and gitoxin are intermediate between these two. The differences are probably a reflection of the differences in the capacity of the proteins to bind these glycosides. This binding ability determines the onset, intensity and duration of action and may be a consequence of the polarity of these compounds, important to their relative solubility and chemical reactivity in water.

Harrison and Wright (15) compared various purified glycosides

---

is these two crucial hydrogen molecules whose position relates to the A:B and C:D ring junctions. Note in III that the hydrogen at C_5 is in the α position as in coprosterol, and that the OH at C_{14} is in the β position. It is not certain whether ring C stays in the more stable "chair" form or assumes the "boat" form as depicted here and suggested by Shoppee (11).

and related compounds in a paper chromatographic system, employing combinations of ethyl hexanol, amyl alcohol, water and formamide on formamide impregnated paper and found consistent differences in the rate of mobility (R_f) of these compounds. Derivatives of lanatoside A were slower moving than corresponding derivatives of lanatoside B, which trailed behind those of lanatoside C. They concluded that the polarity was generally proportional to the number and location of the hydroxyl groups: the addition of an hydroxyl group at C_{12} contributes to a greater increase in polarity than one at C_{16}, presumably because the latter is modified by the beta orientation of the lactone ring. The four hydroxyl groups of an added glucose moiety increase the polarity still further. In Table I, the R_f values for certain glycosides are compared with the intravenous digitalization dose, and with the dissipation rate, which is the percentage of the digitalizing dose that must be replaced daily to maintain digitalization. While these data are compiled from several sources (16, 17, 18), and no claim can be made for their internal consistency, they do illustrate a possible relationship between the polarity of these compounds and their intensity and duration of action.

TABLE I

COMPARISON OF SPEED OF ONSET AND DURATION OF ACTION OF VARIOUS
GLYCOSIDES WITH THEIR CHROMATOGRAPHIC MOBILITY

Glycoside	Time of@ Peak Effect Hours	Average Dose in Mgm. given I.V.* Initial	Maintenance	Rate of* Dissipation % per day	R_f+
Digitoxin	8	2.0	0.15	7	.12
Acetyl Digitoxin	6	1.5	0.2	14	—
Digoxin**	3	2.0	0.4	20	.47
Lanatoside C	1.5	2.0	0.4	20	.89
Strophanthoside	0.5	0.5	0.25	50	very fast

@ From Goodman and Gilman (18)
*From Loeffler, Esselier and Forster (16)
**Figures estimated from Aravanis and Luisada (17) for dosage and dissipation rate
+Values from Harrison and Wright (13) System I.

In summary, the structure common to all cardioactive glycones seems to be a steroid of unique stereoconfiguration in association with a 5- or 6-membered alpha, beta unsaturated lactone ring attached in the equatorial (beta) position at C_{17}. In addition to the two methyl groups at C_{10} and C_{13}, there are at least two beta-hydroxyl groups at C_3 and C_{14}, and sometimes a third, located either at C_{12} or C_{16}. The presence and location of the hydroxyl substituents and the type and length of the sugar chain determine the polarity of the glycoside, and hence the clinically important speed of absorption, strength of cardiac fixation and perhaps the rates of metabolism and excretion.

CLINICAL EFFECTS OF THE PURIFIED GLYCOSIDES

The efforts described at fractionation of the whole leaf digi-talis preparations were born of the practical need for improving the characteristics of this vitally important drug. Knowledge of the potency of the impure preparations had to be based upon bio-assay which has always involved the amount of drug necessary to induce cardiac arrest or ventricular fibrillation in a given animal pre-paration. This is the ultimate toxic effect of the compounds, which is not necessarily related to the desired therapeutic effect and is doubtless influenced by the saponins, tannins, organic acids, and other impurities that were present in the original whole leaf, its decoctions, infusions and tinctures (5). The isolation of the puri-fied glycosides has permitted the use of stable compounds, free of these impurities, which can be measured by weight instead of bio-assay, and which permit more adequate investigation into mechan-isms of digitalis effect. As mentioned above, the chief differences among the various glycosides lie in their speed of action, rate of excretion, and, possibly, incidence of toxic effects.

Long Acting Preparations: *Digitoxin* (Digitalis Nativelle®) clinical trial. It has become the most popular digitalis prepara-tion in use in the U.S.A. today, in large measure due to the en-thusiastic reports of Gold and his co-workers (19). By com-parative studies in patients they showed that 1.0 mgm. of digi-toxin was equivalent to 1.0 gm. of whole leaf digitalis, but that a single digitalization dose of 1.2 mgm. produced toxic symp-toms in only 3% of patients, whereas a presumably correspond-ing 1.5 gm. of whole leaf was known to induce nausea in about 20%. From their studies they concluded that this initial dose could be regularly followed by a maintenance dose of 0.2 mgm. per day. They further established that the effects were equal whether the drug was given orally or intravenously, thus, that intestinal absorption was complete; furthermore, the onset of digitalis effect was early and its effect was cumulative.

There is no doubt that this glycoside presented advantages over the whole leaf preparations, but with the passage of time and development of new glycosides these have faded. The routine pattern of digitalization was frequently unsuccessful, because of underdosage with the initial 1.2 mgm., and ultimate overdosage with 0.2 mgm. for daily maintenance. Furthermore, a considerable variation in patient response still obtained. While gastrointestinal toxicity was minimal, the removal of these warning symptoms led to much more serious toxic symptoms; frequent ventricular arrhythmias and central nervous system symptoms, including coma, were not uncommon. Finally, due to the late recognition of these toxic signs, and the sustained effect of the glycoside, the time required for them to abate on withdrawal of the drug was as much as three weeks. There is a growing conviction that this cardiac glycoside is far from the ideal digitalis preparation (20).

Acetyl Digitoxin, obtained by the enzymatic removal of the terminal glucose on Lanatoside A, has recently received clinical trial in this country (21, 22). The evidence presented seems to support the contention that, while its absorption, speed of action and digitalizing dosage requirements are about the same as those of digitoxin, its rate of excretion and dissipation of toxic symptoms are significantly faster. Again, toxic *signs* often preceded toxic *symptoms.*

Digilanid® is a mixture of the purified lanatosides A, B and C in the same proportion as they occur in the whole leaf; 46%, 17% and 37%, respectively. Here is a combination of fast and slow acting glycosides which combines the advantages of the purified glycosides and the whole leaf. From long experience with this preparation at the University of Chicago Clinics, the authors feel that it is certainly as advantageous as acetyl-digitoxin from the point of view of duration of action and toxic manifestations.

Gitalin is the amorphous mixture left over from the preparation of digitoxin and gitoxin, which, in addition to these two glycosides, contains gitaloxin and strospeside (pg. 11). Batterman (23) has been the chief proponent in the U.S. of the use of this preparation, having found a greater therapeutic range with this mixture than with other cardioglycosides. For example, in comparing gitalin with a whole leaf preparation, he found that doubling the maintenance dose produced toxic manifestations in only one-third, instead of two-thirds of the patients. This has not been confirmed (24), and the significance of Batterman's findings has been challenged (5), though other clinicians have tended to agree with the notion that gitalin can be used successfully in patients who react to other preparations with a toxic before a therapeutic response. The authors are skeptical that such a clinical impression is warranted, and feel that a therapeutic response, however limited and inadequate, precedes toxicity, when purified glycosides are used. If a better therapeutic response is later obtained with another preparation, the tolerance of the patient for digitalis has changed.

European investigators (25, 26) have reported on experiences with *gitaloxin,* the most significant of the pure cardiac glycosides found in the gitalin fraction. A good therapeutic effect was noted, similar in intensity and temporal relationships to digitoxin, but the series was not extensive enough to conclude anything about the toxic/therapeutic ratio. Further studies with this preparation will be awaited with interest.

Fast Acting Preparations: *Lanatoside C,* or its deacetylated form cedilanid D (deslanoside), is the quickest acting of the foxglove glycosides, manifesting its full effect ninety minutes after intravenous injection. *Digoxin,* the same basic glycoside carrying one less glucose molecule than cedilanid D, is similarly effective but with a somewhat slower rate of excretion. These two drugs are less practical for maintenance digitalization, because, unless given in divided dosage throughout the day, the patient may lapse from adequate to toxic digitalis effects in the course of one day. On the other hand, they are extremely helpful in tricky post-operative and similar situations where a prolonged effect may not be needed or even wanted, and where the possibility of toxicity for a few hours may be risked for the gain of assured digitalization.

Acetyl-K-Strophanthidin: The most rapid acting intravenous preparation is the acetylated aglycone of *kombé strophanthus,* 3-beta acetylstrophanthidin. This is not a naturally occurring product, the acetylation being performed synthetically. This material, when injected intravenously in proper dose, shows cardiotonic activity within five minutes, the peak effect occurring within twelve minutes. Its chief use has been in the form of a digitalis tolerance test: the dosage required to induce symptoms or signs of toxicity indicates the state of digitalization, and, because of its rapid dissipation, the signs or symptoms of toxicity do not last long (4). Unfortunately, a few deaths have occurred due to ventricular arrhythmias which developed at the time of peak effect, one even at the hands of the original proponents. Hence, the physician should use this test only in that case where the possible gain in knowledge is worth this risk.

METABOLIC STUDIES

In recent years, the fate of certain purified glycosides, in particular digitoxin, has been studied by the sensitive duck heart technique (27) and with the new precision allowed by radioactive isotope labelling of the drug (28). The findings of these two approaches are in fundamental agreement. As reviewed in a recent symposium (5), both groups found no greater concentration of digitoxin in heart muscle than in any other organ. The time relationships of the drug in various tissues suggested that injected digitoxin disappeared very rapidly from the blood stream (only 6% detected after one hour) and both the unchanged drug and its metabolites are soon found in greatest concentration in the liver, spleen, kidney and gastrointestinal tract. Metabolites appeared in greatest proportion in the liver and spleen. Sixty to 80% of the administered digitoxin was ultimately excreted in the urine, both as unchanged and metabolized digitoxin (about 20% in the first two days), and detectable amounts of metabolites were still present after as many as eighty days in one patient. By the duck heart method, cardioactive digitoxin (and metabolites) was excreted at a rate of 32-44 mcg. per day, when the patient was on a maintenance dose of the drug, an increased amount being recovered when toxicity developed. Helpful as these observations are, they can only provide limited information for understanding the mechanism of action of digitalis derivatives.

It has been well demonstrated that there are several beneficial effects of digitalis upon the heart. Though limited evidence has been presented to show that digitalis has a transient natriuretic effect and, perhaps, relaxes venomotor tone, it remains to be demonstrated that these are of therapeutic significance in the treatment of congestive heart failure. In addition to the dramatic slowing of the ventricular rate in auricular fibrillation, and the conversion of paroxysmal auricular arrhythmias to a normal mechanism, there is a potent increase in the efficiency of the muscular contraction of the failing ventricle. Recent studies with coronary sinus catheterization have confirmed earlier studies on the heart-lung preparation which showed that this improvement in efficiency is accomplished with no increase in utilization of oxygen or aerobic metabolites per unit weight of heart muscle. Similarly, they have confirmed the fact that therapeutic as well as toxic levels of active glycosides effect a loss of potassium from many types of cells and particularly from the cardiac musculature (6, 29). In order to explain these observations, investigators have recently resorted to *in vitro* studies at the subcellular level. Evidence from such studies, some of which are noted below, support the alternative hypotheses that the glycosides act by altering the intracellular ionic environment or, in certain preparations, by changing the state of the contractile protein itself.

Actomyosin, elemental in the contraction of the muscle fibril, draws upon adenosine triphosphate (ATP), or some similar high energy phosphate cycle, for the energy required for contraction. There is apparently no deficiency of high-energy phosphate material in the failing heart, nor have the cardiac glycosides been shown to influence the phase of "energy production." The metabolic defect in the failing heart is an unexplained inability of the contractile protein to utilize the high energy phosphate which continues to be normally produced.

Centrifugal separation of the various cell fractions of heart muscle revealed that labelled digitoxin was located neither in the nuclei, the mitochondria, nor the cell membrane, but diffusely in the cytoplasm, probably in conjunction with actomyosin. At the same time many studies have shown a release of intracellular potassium ions from the cells of the entire body by cardioactive glycosides, and in particular from cardiac muscle. From such observations it has been hypothesized that somehow digitalis partially neutralizes the intracellular ionic cloud of potassium, which normally keeps the resting myosin in its uncontracted state, facilitating the interaction of myosin with ATP and actin, so essential to the contraction of the fibril. Normally the intracellular milieu contains principally potassium, with at least small amounts of sodium and calcium. The calcium is bound but presumably the monovalent ions are free, and in the resting state form a "cloud" about the protein molecules.

On the other hand, it has been shown that digitalis glycosides do influence the tendency of actomyosin in solution to form a gel on standing and apparently enhance its binding of potassium (6). Several workers have observed that, under special circumstances, adenosine triphosphate provoked shortening of actomyosin threads or bands and that this shortening was greater in the presence of the glycosides. Bing's group have even demonstrated that the contractility of actomyosin bands prepared from hearts of patients with congestive failure is less than that from normal hearts. Furthermore, this has been corrected by the addition of digoxin plus calcium to the medium (29).

Whether the digitalis glycosides effect principally the membrane permeability to or the binding capacity of the muscle proteins for certain cations is still at issue. The most attractive hypothesis at present is that the cardioactive glycosides somehow deplete or neutralize the ionic cloud of electrolytes by partially excluding potassium from the cell (or more probably by blocking its complete return during each recovery from contraction), thus achieving a more effective contraction of the muscle fibril at the same energy cost. The reader who would further pursue the evidence for the speculation as to how this group of compounds improves the efficiency of this conversion of chemical to mechanical energy is referred to two recent reviews (6, 29).

Chapter III

ORAL DIURETICS

M ERCURIAL DIURETICS have long been used to control the fluid retention of congestive failure. Calomel was prescribed as a diuretic in the sixteenth century. Intravenous organic mercurials have been recognized as the most potent of diuretic agents since experiences with merbaphen (novasurol) and mersalyl (salyrgan) were reported early in this century. They are still as potent as any diuretic agent and are usually used as a standard for comparison in assessing any new diuretic agent. One example of the modern mercurial compounds is mercaptomerin sodium (Thiomerin®). This is a subcutaneously injectable mercurial diuretic (see figure 4), wherein the mercury is bound through a sulfur (thiol) linkage which apparently reduces local irritation and systemic toxic reactions to a minimum. It has been the organic mercurial of choice for the past ten years (30). It has been possible to train patients with chronic edema to inject themselves periodically, just as diabetics inject insulin, and thus maintain a comfortable state of compensation, sometimes for many years. Attempts to employ mercurial diuretics orally have not met with uniform success for gastric irritation, incomplete absorption and unpredictable results have plagued them all. For recent discussions of mercurial diuretics, the reviews by Sprague (31) and Friedman (32) are recommended.

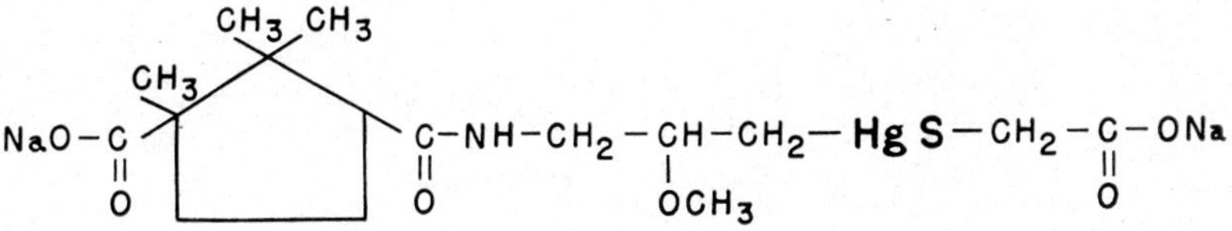

Figure 4. Mercaptomerin sodium (Thiomerin®).

The greater safety and simplicity of *orally* administered diuretic agents hardly needs documentation. At the present time we are seeing what amounts to a revolution in diuretic therapy, in

21

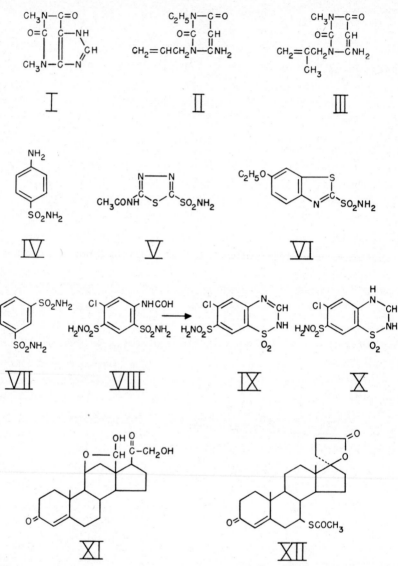

Figure 5. Chemical structure of oral diuretics. I. Theophylline: 1, 3-dimethylxanthine. II. Aminometradine (Mictine®): 1-allyl-3-ethyl-6-amino tetrahydropyrimidinedione. III. Aminoisometradine (Rolicton®): 1-methylallyl 3-methyl-6-amino tetrahydropyrinidinedione. IV. Sulfanilamide: para-aminobenzenesulfonamide. V. Acetazoleamide (Diamox®): 2-acetyl amino-1,3,4 thiadiazole-5-sulfonamide. VI. Ethoxyzolamide (Cardrase®): 6-ethoxy-benzothiadiazole-2-sulfonamide. VII. Benzene-1,3-disulfonamide. VIII. 6-chloro-4-acylamino benzene-1,3-disulfonamide. IX. Chlorothiazide (Diuril®): 6-chloro-

→

particular the therapy of congestive heart failure, because of great new advances in the realm of oral diuretics. Previously, certain theophylline preparations and acid forming salts were used when mild diuresis was indicated. Recently cation exchange resins and certain synthetic uracil compounds presented some gain in the control of edema formation, but they have been largely superceded by the carbonic anhydrase inhibitors, the thiazide derivatives, at first presumed also to be merely carbonic anhydrase inhibitors, and most recently certain synthetic aldosterone inhibitors. The chemical structure of the oral diuretics discussed below can be seen in figure 5.

Aminometradine (II) and aminoisometradine (III), two synthetic compounds, chemically related to theophylline (I) in that they have the same uracil ring, have been shown to have some diuretic potential in the management of congestive heart failure (30). Aminometradine (Mictine®) was superceded by aminoisometradine (Rolicton®) because the former resulted in a higher incidence of gastrointestinal toxicity. While it is clear that these compounds may have greater diuretic potency than theophylline, both have been dramatically overshadowed by acetazoleamide and chlorothiazide.

Carbonic anhydrase inhibitors were developed after World War II following the observation that sulfanilamide (IV) inhibited the enzyme which catalyzes the reversible formation of carbonic acid from the solution of CO_2 in H_2O:

$$1) \quad CO_2 + H_2O \rightleftharpoons H \cdot HCO_3$$

A systematic study of synthetic heterocyclic sulfonamides led to the discovery of acetazoleamide (V) (Diamox®) which is a potent inhibitor of carbonic anhydrase in many organ systems of the body (33). Perhaps the most important of these organ effects is exerted on the renal tubule where much of the acid-base balance

---

7-sulfamyl 1, 2, 4-benzothiadiazine-1, 1-dioxide. X. Hydrochlorothiazide (Esidrix®) : 6-chloro-3,4-dihydro-7-sulfamyl-2H-1,2,4-benzothiadizine-1,1-dioxide. XI. Aldosterone-(lactal form) : 18-oxocorticosterone or 11β,21-dihydro-3,20-dioxo-4-pregnen-18-al. XII. Spironolactone (Aldactone®) : 3 (3-oxo-7α-acetyl-thio-17 β-hydroxy-4-androsten-17α-yl) propionic acid lactone.

of the blood is regulated. Other effects include a reduction in the secretion of acid by the stomach and of bicarbonate by the pancreas and an inhibition of the carbonic anhydrase activity of the brain and the eye. These latter effects provide useful anticonvulsant and antiglaucomatous properties of the drug.

In reviews on the renal regulation of acid-base balance, Pitts has pointed out the importance of carbonic anhydrase in controlling the excretion of titratible acid and "fixed" base and in the conservation of sodium (34, 35). The dissociation of

$$2)\quad H_2CO_3 \rightleftharpoons H^+ + HCO_3^-$$

provides protons (hydrogen ions) within the tubular cell which may exchange for sodium and perhaps contribute to the tubular excretion of the ammonium ion in the formation of the tubular urine. Thus, when H^+ availability is limited by carbonic anhydrase blockade, these two effects are diminished: more sodium and less ammonium are then excreted. Theoretically, the inhibition of carbonic anhydrase activity may also limit the reabsorption of HCO_3^- at the tubular cell; thus, both Na^+ and HCO_3^- excretion are enhanced.

Thus, with significant carbonic anhydrase blockade, an alkaline urine rich in Na^+ is excreted. With this there is an increased excretion of water, HCO_3^- and to some extent K^+. There is no increase in excretion of the anions Cl^- and $PO_4^=$, but there is a decrease in the excretion of NH_4^+ and titratable acid. Consequently, from the loss of cations, Na^+ and K^+, a metabolic acidosis may develop. With continuous administration of acetazolamide, the diuresis is soon halted because of depletion of bicarbonate stores and the associated metabolic acidosis. Production of a similar acidosis by the prior administration of NH_4Cl will nullify the action of acetazoleamide for, in an acid medium, carbonic anhydrase is no longer necessary to facilitate reaction 1) (36). Thus acetazoleamide has a self-limiting diuretic action, as do the acidifying salts, and must be given intermittently to be effective. In normal subjects the effect of a single dose of acetazolamide lasts 8 to 12 hours so that administration once a day may be considered intermittent dosage; in patients with congestive failure the effect is similar, in the absence of renal disease (37). Some authors feel that rest periods of one or two days a week may provide more effective and more economical maintenance of the diuretic action (38). The metabolic acidosis resulting from the administration of acetazoleamide, as with the administration of NH_4Cl, is reported to potentiate mercurial diuresis. Though both of these agents effect a metabolic acidosis, an acid urine results from adequate dosage of ammonium chloride.

The patient who already has a respiratory acidosis may be benefited by continuous carbonic anhydrase inhibition in that the elevated partial pressure of CO_2 in plasma will be reduced, and the mental state improved. In the presence of normal tubular function, HCO_3^- reabsorption is soon restored to normal as noted above, yet the increased efficiency of CO_2 exhalation persists (39). This is probably due to improved sensitivity of the respiratory center to arterial CO_2, for the effect of carbonic anhydrase inhibition in the red cell is to impair transport of CO_2 from the red cells to the alveolus so that, as is seen in the dog, arterial CO_2 should rise and alveolar CO_2 fall. In the human, no such consistent effects are seen in normal subjects. It would seem that in man the effects upon CO_2 transport in the blood are modest and variable except when that transport system is taxed, as during exercise or pulmonary insufficiency. In the former case the arterial pCO_2 rises, in the latter it falls. There is as yet no good explanation for this paradox (40).

Recently the 6-ethoxy derivative of benzothiazole-5-sulfonamide (VI) (Cardrase®) has been reported to be less toxic and more potent, per unit weight, than acetazoleamide (41). The former claim is not based on convincing evidence, and the latter claim has little merit as a practical consideration. Actually, toxic idiosyncrasy to the diuretic dose of acetazoleamide (Diamox®) is quite infrequent and rarely serious, except in the presence of advanced liver disease when ammonium toxicity can be precipitated or aggravated (see page 28).

Chlorothiazide was developed by Novello and Sprague in a purposeful search for greater diuretic activity among synthetic aromatic sulfonamide derivatives (42). These were found to have an inhibitory effect on carbonic anhydrase somewhat weaker than acetazoleamide, but an unexpectedly high order of diuretic activity was discovered among certain derivatives of benzene -1, 3-disulfonamide (VII). Substitution of halogen, amino or acylamino groups onto the benzene ring enhanced the diuretic activity. The addition of an acylamino group in the position *ortho* to one of the sulfamyl groups was found to lead to a second ring formation and a cyclized derivative, as seen in figure 5, VIII and IX. The 6-chloro derivative was found to be most potent, and was called chlorothiazide (Diuril®).

This group of compounds differed from acetazoleamide in producing a copious diuresis of Cl^- and $PO_4^\equiv$ ions as well as Na^+, HCO_3^- and K^+ (43, 44). The diuretic effect is similar to that of a mercurial diuretic, though affecting K^+ excretion to a greater degree. The compound is excreted in the urine essentially unchanged, and its effect is not quickly self-limiting as in the case of acetazoleamide but continues to be manifest with round-the-clock administration. With continuous intensive use, however, the resulting electrolyte depletion is often reflected in the same hypochloremic alkalosis with more or less hypokalemia seen after strenuous and repeated mercurial diuresis. Of greater interest is the fact that a mercurial injection and oral chlorothiazide combined will produce a more copious diuresis than either one alone, suggesting that different mechanisms may be involved in the action of the two compounds.

Pitts and co-workers (45) studied the single and combined effects of *chlormerodrin* (a mercurial diuretic), chlorothiazide and acetazoleamide in maximally effective dosage under carefully controlled conditions in dogs. Chlorothiazide induced natriuresis and kaliuresis with an alkaline urine rich in HCO_3^-. Though the cation and water excretion were more profuse, the alkalinity and bicarbonate excretion attributable to carbonic anhydrase activity was less prominent than that seen with acetazoleamide. The combined effect of chlormerodrin and chlorothiazide, in maximum effective dose, was a simple summation of their individual diuretic effects. Since even the combined effect blocked less than 50 percent of the tubular reabsorption of Na^+, it was concluded that at least three enzyme systems must be involved in its renal tubular transport: one must be sensitive to mercurials (the succinic dehydrogenase system has been implicated), another to chlorothiazide, a third to neither. Of course, it must be admitted that the effected enzymes may all supply energy to the same basic transport mechanism for Na^+.

Further comparisons between the effects of mercurial and chlorothiazide diuresis on electrolyte excretion in three normal human subjects were made by Heinemann, Demartini and Laragh (46). At similar high rates of urine flow, chlorothiazide administration induced a reduction in glomerular filtration not seen with the mercurial diuretic; total solute excretion, in particular potassium excretion, was greater; hence urinary osmolarity was also greater than with mercurial diuresis. In other words, the clearance of that water not osmotically obligated to solute, the "free water" of the urine, was increased to a much greater extent by mercurial than by chlorothiazide diuresis. This difference in action can be explained by assuming that mercurials block only proximal tubular reabsorption of these electrolytes, while chlorothiazide blocks both proximal and distal tubular reabsorption. This follows from the hypothesis that water and electrolytes are isosmotically reabsorbed in the proximal tubule, whereas Na^+ and Cl^- may be selectively reabsorbed in the distal tubule to leave unattached "free water" in the excreted urine. Inhibition of this distal tubular reabsorption of electrolytes by chlorothiazide then would be expected to lessen the amount of "free water" ultimately excreted.

Hypopotassemia can be produced by chronic chlorothiazide administration, perhaps more frequently than with mercurial therapy, and particularly in the patient with liver or renal disease who is on a restricted sodium intake. Potassium depletion does not always obtain when chlorothiazide is given, but, since the ancillary determinants of thiazide-induced hypokalemia are incompletely understood, potassium supplementation is probably wise (44). The diuretic effect of chlorothiazide is different from that of a mercurial diuretic in that it is not substantially enhanced by the preinduction of an ammonium chloride acidosis, nor as easily suppressed by an hypochloremic alkalosis (46). Consequently, chlorothiazide may still operate where mercurials will no longer effect a diuresis. Furthermore, situations may arise where these diuretics combined may be preferred to either one; a mercurial diuresis may sometimes aid in repair of dilutional hyponatremia, while chlorothiazide may not, if the intimations of Heinemann, et al. (46) can be confirmed.

Because no renal irritation has resulted from chlorothiazide it is safer and, at times, more effective than mercurial diuretics in renal disease. It is effective as a hypotensive agent, especially in conjunction with other hypotensive agents, but less consistently when used alone. This effect is accompanied by an initial reduction in plasma volume and may be related to the natriuretic property of the drug (43).

Aside from the ease with which electrolyte imbalance may be induced, the only important adverse effect of chlorothiazide, as with acetazoleamide, has been the precipitation of coma in patients with advanced liver disease. This is apparently due to retention of NH_4^+, which would ordinarily be metabolized by the liver, with a consequent rise in blood level. Since this has been correctible by the administration of neomycin, NH_3 production by the intestinal bacteria must play an important role (47). In a few instances an elevation of blood urea nitrogen has been observed as a consequence of chlorothiazide effect in hypertensive patients. This has been regularly associated with a marked hypotensive effect and has been corrected by restoration of blood pressure to pre-treatment values, so that it is doubtless due to excretory failure (44).

Dihydrochlorothiazide, or 6-chloro-3,4 dihydro -7- sulfamyl— 2H—12,4- benzothiadiazine, has recently been marketed as Esidrix® (X, in figure 3). This differs from the above compound only in the saturation of the double bond in the thiadiazine ring. This product is ten to twenty times as potent as chlorothiazide by weight, and yet has an LD_{50} in rats almost twice as great. Thus, the manufacturer claims a more potent, less toxic product. Aside from the dubious advantage that 50 mgm. tablets can be administered in place of 500 mgm. tablets, there appears to be no qualitative difference between the effects with unsaturated and saturated heterocyclic rings, except that the former seems to have a weaker inhibitory effect upon carbonic anhydrase. Claims that the latter will effect diuresis when the former fails, and that it will have a greater hypotensive effect with less potassium loss have not been borne out by clinical investigation (48).

Somewhat similar claims are being made at the time of going to press for *Flumethiazide* (Ademol®) a 6-trifluoromethyl-7- sulfamyl-1,2,4-benzothiadiazide-1,1-dioxide. Unless the original claims that kaliuresis is less with this derivative than with the other two (49, 50) can be substantiated, this derivative will also provide little advantage over chlorothiazide.

Aldosterone Antagonists: In the introduction it was intimated that an increased aldosterone excretion may be part of the syndrome of congestive heart failure. There is no agreement as to whether this is a cause or effect of the edema formation in that condition and, in either case, what relationship this may have to therapy. Is it a prominent early feature of the development of fluid retention or a late consequence of the sodium restriction prescribed for the patient (51)? The answers to these questions will soon be forthcoming for there has recently been made available a series of potent and apparently innocuous compounds, the spirolactones, which appear to act as antagonists of the renal effect of aldosterone on electrolyte balance (52). The latest in the spirolactone series, at the time of going to press, is spironolactone (Aldactone®), 3- (3-oxo-7 alpha-acetylthio-17 beta-hydroxy-4-androsten-17 alpha-yl) propionic acid lactone, (Figure 3, XII: compare with aldosterone, XI). One established stimulus to aldosterone excretion by the adrenal glands is sodium deprivation (51). The spirolactones have no effect upon urinary electrolytes in a normal subject amply supplied with salt: in the same subject depleted of salt, when aldosterone activity becomes prominent, these agents provoke a sodium diuresis with potassium retention (53). The spirolactones do not effect the excretion of aldosterone in primary aldosteronism, though they completely reverse the renal retention of sodium. Ammonium and potassium excretion may actually be decreased (54). Other antidiuretic substances often excreted in increased amounts in the urine of patients with edema, are not necessarily influenced by these agents.

In the few reported cases with cirrhosis and ascites or congestive heart failure with edema who have been treated by spirolactones, there is quite universally a diuresis of water, sodium and chloride. This has not always been substantial enough to result in weight loss, however, (54) and in stubborn cases of edema with dilutional hyponatremia it is doubtful that even these synthetic steroids will often help. It will certainly be some time before the proper place of these agents in the treatment of advanced congestive heart failure will be known. It has been pointed out, however, that, inasmuch as this is the only known drug to effect a potassium retention in the face of a natriuresis, it will probably be a useful adjunct to the other diuretic agents already mentioned above (55).

The mechanism of action of the spirolactones seems to be a competitive inhibition of aldosterone and/or deoxycorticosterone at the renal tubule. This is based upon the fact that, in addition to their chemical similarity to aldosterone, they oppose its effects on electrolyte balance without influencing its urinary excretion (51).

Chapter IV

SERUM ELECTROLYTES AND
HEART FAILURE

WITH THE DEVELOPMENT of the flame photometer during World War II, it became possible to do frequent electrolyte determinations in clinical practice. It soon became evident that abnormal electrolyte patterns developed in patients who were being treated for severe congestive failure. A patient who had been responding satisfactorily to periodic mercurial injections might suddenly fail to respond. Most frequently a low Cl^-, high CO_2 and perhaps a somewhat low K^+ would be found in the serum. This *hypochloremic alkalosis* is also the most common electrolyte imbalance consequent to chlorothiazide therapy. It can be corrected in either case by the administration of ammonium chloride, or by strong carbonic anhydrase inhibition. In some cases supplementary potassium may also be indicated, but this is not usually necessary.

Dilutional Hyponatremia. Much discussion ten years ago centered around the "low salt syndrome" which occurred in patients with heart failure who had become unresponsive to the usual diuretic measures, and which was attributed at that time to severe sodium depletion reinforced by a low salt intake. In this situation serum sodium as well as chloride was low while the pH and CO_2 were normal or low. With increasing experience it became evident that most of these patients were not sodium deficient, for total body sodium was still increased. Furthermore, they died all the sooner when hypertonic saline was administered. Careful balance studies have revealed that the total body sodium was still elevated; formed elements as well as chemical constituents of the blood were simply diluted by excessive water retention. This then became known as *dilutional hyponatremia,* and it has been recently observed that it could be corrected when a complicating intercurrent infection, pulmonary infarction or severe arrhythmia could be reversed (56). It has been seen sometimes in untreated con-

31

gestive failure when a reversal to normal occurred with adequate digitalization.

A situation may still arise wherein sodium depletion provokes hyponatremia, though it rarely, if ever, is found in the presence of edema. The circulating blood volume contracts, all evidence of congestion subsides and the hematocrit rises as a disproportion in water and sodium develops and hyponatremia occurs. It is only in this set of circumstances that supplementary sodium may relieve the hyponatremia. Other instances of hyponatremia in heart failure difficult to explain by either sodium dilution or sodium depletion have been observed. A more comprehensive discussion of electrolyte disorders may be found in a review by Friedberg (57).

Serum Potassium and Digitalis Toxicity. *Hypo-* and *hyperpotassemia* are particularly serious in these patients because of the apparent antagonistic effect, alluded to in the second chapter, between potassium and digitalis. It is still unresolved whether the serum potassium, or intracellular potassium or their difference may be the more fundamental parameter involved, but as intracellular potassium is too difficult a determination for clinical use, most references have been made to the serum potassium. The loss of potassium with a mercurial diuretic or chlorothiazide may produce more or less transient symptoms of digitalis toxicity in the fully digitalized patient, and the patient whose maintenance dose of digitalis is established during hyperpotassemia may become intoxicated when that condition is reversed. It has also been amply confirmed since the clinical observations of Sampson (58) that intravenous potassium will correct arrhythmias and even subjective symptoms due to toxic levels of digitalis. This effect lasts only as long as the intravenous infusion continues, except when body stores were previously depleted.

A possible advance in the treatment of digitalis toxicity has come with the introduction of methods by which the chelation of ionized blood calcium is possible. Though no abnormality in calcium balance is known to exist in heart failure, hypocalcemia has an effect upon myocardial excitability similar to hyperpotassemia. By the judicious intravenous administration of magnesium or sodium ethylene diamine tetra acetate (EDTA) Gubner and Kallman (59) were able to accomplish sufficient reduction in ionizable serum calcium to correct signs and symptoms of digitalis toxicity in several patients for several days at a time. Later workers (60) have found a less sustained reversal of toxicity by this technique, an observation which the authors can confirm, but it is nevertheless a useful therapy especially in certain situations where the administration of potassium may be undesirable.

CONCLUSION

Digitalis has survived for 175 years as the bulwark of treatment in congestive heart failure, yet, as we learn more about its components and their mechanism of action, we are still searching for a more ideal preparation. Its use is complicated by the tremendous and unpredictable variation in the optimum dosage needed from one patient to the next and, because of electrolyte shifts induced by more recent diuretic agents, in the same patient from time to time. As a corollary to the extension of life afforded to cardiac patients by modern usage of digitalis derivatives and potent diuretics, their continued management becomes increasingly complicated. The physician must be increasingly alert to incidental complications that may lead to alterations in electrolyte balance which may further influence the strength of the digitalized heart and the volume of blood it must propel. Thus, the application of new synthetic compounds advanced through the ingenuity of the organic chemist requires detailed attention to the alterations in the body chemistry of the individual patient.

REFERENCES

1. Best, C. H. and Taylor, N. B.: *The Physiological Basis of Medical Practice*. Sixth Ed., The Williams and Wilkins Co., Baltimore, 1955.
2. Vander, A. J., Malvin, R. L., Wilde, W. S. and Sullivan, L. P. Editorial: Re-examination of Salt and Water Retention in Congestive Heart Failure. Significance of Renal Filtration Fraction. Am. J. Med., 25: 497, 1958.
3. Withering, W.: An Account of the Foxglove and Some of its Medical Uses. Reprinted in Medical Classics, 2: 305, 1937.

4. Lown, B. and Levine, S. A.: *Current Concepts in Digitalis Therapy.* Little, Brown and Company, Boston, 1954.
5. Dimond, E. G. (Editor) : *Digitalis.* Charles C Thomas, Springfield, Illinois, 1957.
6. Hajdu, S. and Leonard, E.: The Cellular Basis of Cardiac Glycoside Action. Pharmacol. Rev., *11:* 173, 1959.
7. Stoll, A.: *The Cardiac Glycosides.* The Pharmaceutical Press, London, 1937.
8. Stoll, A.: The Cardiactive Glycosides. J. Pharm. and Pharmacol., *1:* 849, 1949.
9. Aldrich, B. J., Frith, M. L. and Wright, S. E.: Paper Chromatographic Detection of New Constituents of Digitalis Lanata. J. Pharm. and Pharmacol., *8:* 1042, 1956.
10. Fieser, L. F. and Fieser, M.: *Steroids.* Rheinhold Publ. Corp. N. Y., N. Y., 1959.
11. Shoppee, C. W.: *Chemistry of the Steroids.* Academic Press Inc., New York, N. Y., 1958.
12. Haack, E., Kaiser, F., Gube, M. and Spingler, H.: Chemistry of the "Gitalin Fraction." Arznemittel-Forschung., *6:* 176, 1956.
13. Jensen, K. B.: Chemical and Biological of Digitalis Purpurea Acta. Pharmacolog. and Toxicol., *13:* 381, 1957.
14. Spratt, J. L. and Okita, G.: Protein Binding of Radioactive Digitoxin. J. Pharmacol. and Exper. Therap., *124:* 109, 1958.
15. Harrison, J. and Wright, S. E.: Paper Chromatography of Some Cardiac Glycosides. J. Pharm. and Pharmacol., *9:* 92, 1957.
16. Loeffler, W., Esselier, A. F. and Forster, G.: Acetyldigitoxin. ein neues herzwirksames Glykosid. Klinische-Pharmakologische Untersuchungen. Schweiz. med. Wohnschr., *83:* 290, 1953.
17. Aravanis, C. and Luisada, A. A.: Clinical Comparison of Six Digitalis Preparations by the Parenteral Route. The Am. J. of Cardiol., *1:* 706, 1958.
18. Goodman, L. S. and Gilman, A.: *The Pharmacological Basis of Therapeutics.* Second Edition. The Macmillan Co., N. Y., N. Y., 1955.
19. Gold, H., Cattell, McK., Modell, W., Kwit, N. T., Kramer, M. L. and Zahm, W.: Clinical Studies on Digitoxin (Digitaline Nativelle) J. Pharmacol. and Exper. Ther., *82:* 187, 1944.
20. Marriott, H. J. L. Editorial: The Ascendancy of Digitoxin and Renaissance of Gitalin. Ann. Int. Med., *40:* 820, 1954.
21. Shash, S. J., Rubler, S. and Weston, R. E.: Clinical Studies on a

New Cardiac Glycoside, Acetyldigitoxin. J. A. M. A., *161:* 1543, 1956.

22. Gold, H. and Bellet, S.: Acetyl Digitoxin in the Treatment of Heart Failure. New Eng. J. Med., *256:* 536, 1957.
23. Batterman, R. C., De Graff, A. C., and Rose, O. A.: The Therapeutic Range of Gitalin (Amorphous) Compared with Other Digitalis Preparations. Circulation, *5:* 201, 1952.
24. Bryfogle, J. W., Santilli, T., Saltzman, H. A. and Bellet, S.: Therapeutic and Toxic Indices of Digitalis: A Comparative Study of Gitalin and Digitalis Leaf. New Eng. J. Med., *256:* 767, 1957.
25. Kroetz, C. und Foerster, K.: Die Klinische Wirkungsanalyse der "Gitalins" am Herzinsuffizienten Kranken. Arznemittel-Forschungen, *6:* 189, 1956.
26. Cloetens, W., DeMey, D., Dernier, J. Georges, A.: Etude Chimique, Pharmacologique et Clinique de la Gitaline Amorphe et de la Neo-Gitaline. Bruxelles-Medical, *38:* 765, 1958.
27. Friedman, M., St. George, S. and Bine, R. Jr.: The Behavior and Fate of Digitoxin in the Experimental Animal and Man. Medicine, *33:* 15, 1954.
28. Okita, G. T.: Studies with Radioactive Digitalis. J. Am. Geriatric Soc., *5:* 163, 1957.
29. Bing, R. J.: Some Physiological Actions of Digitalis. See Ref. 5. Page 20.
30 Warshaw, L. J., Gold, H., Modell, W., Grenier, T. H., Kwit, N. T., Gluck, J. L., Otto, H. L., Kramer, M. L. and Zahm, W.: Subdermal Injection as Mode of Administration of Mercurial Diuretics. J. A. M. A., *145:* 1049, 1951.
31. Sprague, J.: The Chemistry of Diuretics. Ann. N.Y. Acad. Sci., *71:* 328, 1958.
32. Friedman, H. L.: Relationship between Chemical Structures and Biological Activity in Mercurial Compounds. idem, *65:* 461, 1957.
33. Roblin, R. O. Jr.: The Preparation of Heterocyclic Sulfonamids. J. Am. Chem. Soc., *72:* 890, 1950.
34. Pitts, R. F.: Acid-Base Regulation by the Kidneys. Am. J. Med., *9:* 356, 1950.
35. Pitts, R. F.: Some Reflections on Mechanism of Action of Diuretics. idem, *24:* 745, 1958.
36. Maren, T. H.: The Effects of Metabolic Acidosis on the Response to Diamox. Bull. Johns Hopkins Hospital., *98:* 159, 1956.

37. Friedberg, C. K., Taymor, R., Miner, J. B. and Halpern, M.: The Use of Diamox, a Carbonic Anhydrase Inhibitor, in Congestive Heart Failure. New Eng. J. Med., *248:* 883, 1953.
38. Braveman, W. S., Dexter, R. L., and Rubin, A. L.: Diamox as an Oral Diuretic in Ambulatory Cardiac Patients. Am. Heart J., *54:* 284, 1957.
39. Nodell, J.: The Effects of the Carbonic Anhydrase Inhibitor "6063." On Electrolytes and Acid Base Balance in Two Normal Subjects and Two Patients with Respiratory Acidosis. J. Clin. Investigation, *32:* 622, 1953.
40. Goldston, M. and Geller, J.: Effects of Aminophylline and Diamox Alone and Together on Respiration and Acid-Base Balance and on Respiratory Response to Carbon Dioxide in Pulmonary Emphysema. Am. J. Med., *23:* 183, 1957.
41. Gold, H., Greiner, T. H., Warshaw, L., Kwit, N. T. and Ganz, A.: Diuretic Action of Two Carbonic Anhydrase Inhibitors in Congestive Failure. J. A. M. A., *167:* 814, 1958.
42. Novello, F. C. and Sprague, J. M.: Benzothiadiazine Dioxides as Novel Diuretics. J. Am. Chem. Soc., *79:* 2028, 1957.
43. Ford, R. V., Moyer, J. H. and Spurr, C. L.: Clinical and Laboratory Observations on Chlorothiazide (Diuril) : An Orally Effective Non-Mercurial Diuretic Agent. A.M.A. Arch. Int. Med., *100:* 582, 1957.
44. Symposium: Chlorothiazide and other Diuretic Agents. Ed. John V. Taggart. Ann. N. Y. Acad. Sci., *71:* 321, 1958.
45. Pitts, R. F., Krück, F., Lozano, R., Taylor, D. W., Heldenreich, O. P. A. and Kessler, R. H.: Studies on the Mechanism of Diuretic Action of Chlorothiazide. J. Pharmacol. and Exp. Ther., *123:* 89, 1958.
46. Heinemann, H. O., Demartini, F. E., and Laragh, J. H.: The Effect of Chlorothiazide on Renal Excretion of Electrolytes and Free Water. Am. J. Med., *26:* 853, 1959.
47. Mackie, J. E., Stormont, J. M., Hollister, R. M. and Davidson, C. S.: Production of Impending Coma by Chlorothiazide and its Prevention by Antibiotics. New Eng. J. Med., *259:* 1151, 1958.
48. Fleming, P. R., Zilva, J. F., Bayliss, R. I. S. and Pirkis, J.: Hydrochlorothiazide: A Comparison with Chlorothiazide. Lancet, *1:* 1218, 1959.
49. Bodi, T., Fuchs, M., Irie, S. and Moyer, J. H.: Further Observations on Flumethiazide, a New Oral Diuretic Agent. Am. J. Cardiol., *4:* 464, 1959.

50. Ford, R. V.: Comparative Effects on Urinary Electrolyte Excretion Following Two Benzothiadiazine Diuretics, Flumethiazide and Chlorothiazide. Am. J. Med. Sci., *239:* 165, 1960.

51. Farrell, G.: Regulation of Aldosterone Secretion. Physiol. Rev., *38:* 709, 1958.

52. Kagawa, C. M., Cella, J. A. and Van Arman, C. G.: Action of New Steroids in Blocking Effects of Aldosterone and Deoxycorticosterone on Salt. Science, *126:* 1015, 1957.

53. Liddle, G. W.: Sodium Diuresis Induced by Steroidal Antagonists of Aldosterone. Science, *126:* 1016, 1957.

54. Kerr, D. N. S., Read, A. E., Haslam, R. M. and Sherlock, S.: The Use of a Steroidal Spirolactone in the Treatment of Ascites in Hepatic Cirrhosis. Lancet, *2:* 1084, 1958.

55. Laragh, J.: The Use of Diuretics in the Treatment of Congestive Heart Failure. Postgrad. Med., *25:* 528, 1959.

56. Weston, R. E., Grossman, J., Borun, E. R. and Hanenson, I. B.: The Pathogenesis and Treatment of Hyponatremia in Congestive Heart Failure. Am. J. Med., *25:* 558, 1958.

57. Friedberg, C. K.: Fluid and Electrolyte Disturbances in Heart Failure and their Treatment. Circulation, *16:* 437, 1957.

58. Sampson, J. J., Alberton, E. C., and Kondo, B.: The Effect on Man of Potassium Administration in Relation to Digitalis Glycosides, with Special Reference to Blood Serum Potassium, the Electrocardiogram and Ectopic Beats. Am. Hrt. J., *26:* 164, 1943.

59. Gubner, R. S. and Kallman, H.: Treatment of Digitalis Toxicity by Chelation of Serum Calcium. Am. J. Med. Sci., *234:* 136, 1957.

60. Kabakow, B. and Brothers, M. J.: The Effects of Induced Hypocalcemia on Myocardial Irritability and Conductivity. Arch. Int. Med., *101:* 1029, 1958.

SECTION II
THROMBOSIS

Chapter I

THROMBOSIS

In this section, the pathogenesis of thrombosis will be briefly reviewed. This will be followed by discussions of blood coagulation and hemostasis, and anticoagulant and thrombolytic drugs, to underscore the likely roles of the former in thrombosis, and clarify the actions of the latter in preventing thrombosis or ameliorating its consequences. Our experience over a decade with oral anti-coagulant drugs for the long-term treatment of myocardial infarction will also be recounted.

Blood in the healthy circulation is fluid, but in the course of numerous diseases a portion may gel or otherwise solidify and form a thrombus. Thrombosis, the formation of thrombi, may occur anywhere in the cardiovascular system. It appears to depend upon the abnormal interplay of the numerous soluble and particulate factors involved in fibrin formation, and the tissue factors involved in hemostasis. A thrombus may either remain lodged at the site of origin or fracture and break loose to circulate in the blood as a thromboembolus, which may ultimately impact in a vessel too small to permit its passage and obstruct the flow of blood. Thrombi or thromboemboli of sufficient size and in strategic sites may compromise the nutrition of an organ, producing organ dysfunction, severe morbidity or even death.

Morphology. A thrombus has a varied morphology depending upon its age, the circulatory forces shaping it, and the character of the vessel in which it occurs; but frequently it appears histologically as a blend of a fibrin clot and enmeshed formed elements of the blood. It may contain many platelet clumps or few, numerous erythrocyte masses or none. It may be laminated or homogeneous. It may be spherical, obliterating the lumen completely, or crescentic, permitting a limited flow; or it may be irregularly attached to the endothelium at several points. Fibrin is easily demonstrated

41

in the early lesion but loses its staining quality or is lost in older lesions.

Incidence. Arterial and venous thrombosis account for greater mortality and morbidity than is generally appreciated. Hunter, et al. (1) demonstrated that more than half the autopsies examined had anatomic evidence of deep vein thrombosis of the lower extremities, and Ophüls (2) pointed out that ten percent of 3000 autopsy cases had arterial, venous or intracardiac thrombosis. Hicks and Warren (3) analyzed 100 autopsy cases with cerebral infarct and found forty percent were the result of thrombotic vascular occlusion. Wright et al. (4) reported that about 75% of acute myocardial infarctions seen at autopsy were the result of thrombosis of a coronary artery, though others have found as low as fifty percent based on thrombosis (5, 6). It is clear that thrombosis is one of the most serious and common diseases challenging the physician.

THE PATHOGENESIS OF THROMBOSIS

Since Virchow's time, it has been held that blood stasis, vessel injury and blood hypercoagulability are important factors predisposing to thrombosis. Experiments in the past hundred years have concentrated on evaluating the role of stasis and vessel injury because of their easy experimental manipulation. The results of many of these experiments are in great part supportive of the notion that stasis and vessel injury are contributive rather than of first importance in the production of thrombosis. Hypercoagulability of blood, less easy to measure, has come under critical investigation only in recent years, and gives good promise of providing a still better insight into the pathogenesis of thrombosis.

Stasis and Injury in Venous Thrombosis. Deep vein thrombosis is common clinically and at autopsy in the inactive elderly patient, the bedridden, post-operative or puerperal patient, and the obese (1). This is attributed to a decreased venous flow which may result from varicosities, pelvic vein compression or an otherwise sluggish circulation. The slow circulation theoretically results in hypoxia which predisposes to endothelial injury, platelet deposition on the injured endothelium, the release of thromboplastic material from platelets and injured endothelium, and fibrinolysin inhibition by the vessel lining (7), all of which ultimately result in thrombosis. In the postoperative and puerperal patient, increased platelet numbers and platelet adhesiveness are thought further to predispose to thrombosis. The features of the above which have been established are the postoperative slowing of venous flow, the platelet deposition, and the increase in platelet numbers and adhesiveness (8); the rest is speculation.

Numerous experimental observations trying to evaluate the role of blood stasis in thrombosis indicate that stasis alone may not be responsible for thrombosis (9). Furthermore, in spite of teaching to the contrary, there is no uniform agreement that the incidence of thrombosis in patients who are ambulated early in the postoperative period is appreciably less than that prior to the time early ambulation became popular (8).

If the role of blood stasis is unsettled, so is that of vessel injury. Presumably injury of the endothelial surface promotes coagulation, yet removal of the endothelial lining of ligated segments does not necessarily result in thrombosis (10). Furthermore, it is quite difficult to induce venous thrombosis by simple injury, with any regularity, except by the injection of caustic solutions.

Stasis and Injury in Arterial Thrombosis. It is generally held that slowing of the stream must be important in arterial as well as venous thrombosis. Supporting evidence are the observations of a decreased flow rate in cerebral artery disease, in which cerebral thrombosis is so common (11), and the frequent development of thrombotic arterial occlusion during sleep, presumably at a time of least flow. These relationships are by no means constant or unequivocal. In fact the total *resting* coronary blood flow (ml./min.) has been measured in patients with coronary sclerosis (evidenced by angina pectoris), and is not less but slightly greater than normal. Also, the perfusing pressures and peripheral resistance are normal (12). This is indirect evidence for the widespread collateral circulation known to develop in the sclerotic coronary arterial tree (13). Presumably, as more of the blood flow is carried by the expanding collateral branches, the flow through a narrowed branch becomes correspondingly less, reaching a minimum at periods of least coronary blood flow. However, fatal coronary thrombosis frequently occurs in those hearts with least collateral coronary circulation, and, by these assumptions, with the most rapid flow of blood through the narrowed arterial segment. In such cases we can postulate *other* mechanisms, as outlined on page 103; but, if these occur as infrequently as is now thought, a large proportion of spontaneous coronary thromboses remain which are not easily explained by stasis.

Intimal injury is thought to promote thrombosis by either release of thrombogenic agents or disturbance of the blood flow. Evidence in support of the former remains to be established, and the effect of eddy currents and turbulence on hypercoagulability has to the present defied investigation.

Vascular Injury and Hypercoagulation. Thrombosis is usually associated with underlying vascular disease: it is common in phlebitis, arteritis and the arterioscleroses. The story is not this simple however. For while it is well known that ulcerated atheromatous plaques may underlie arterial thrombi (14) and arterial thrombi are seldom found in non-atherosclerotic vessels, thrombi may be absent from severely sclerotic or even ulcerated vessels (2). Furthermore, thrombosis may occur in the absence of histologically demonstrable vessel injury, presumably in consequence of blood hypercoagulability: e.g., it is common in patients with hemoglobinopathy, polycythemia vera, thrombotic thrombocytopenic purpura, familial thrombophilia, and neoplasm. Knowledge of the relative contributions of vascular disease and hypercoagulability to thrombogenesis is meager and these observations are too contradictory to satisfy the simple hypothesis that vascular injury induces thrombosis.

It might well be, as in the example of atherosclerosis, that the vascular injury and the thrombosis represent two distinct diseases of different but related etiologies. Support of such a concept is suggested by the fact that both the coagulation of the blood and atherosclerosis may be influenced by changes in the fat level in the blood. So far this common ground is speculative and whether or not this connection is borne out remains for future research to decide.

It is worthy of emphasis that there remains a distinct if unproven possibility that primary changes can occur in the blood itself which promote thrombosis, and that, though stasis and injury have roles in thrombogenesis, potent procoagulants may be generated by unsuspected pathways not presently recognized in coagulation or hemostasis.

Chapter II

BLOOD COAGULATION AND HEMOSTASIS

T HE PROVEN VALUE of anticoagulants in the treatment of thrombotic disease is strong evidence that altered blood coagulation plays an important role in thrombosis. The fact that they are not always successful and that thrombosis very frequently occurs on the injured lining of vessels or in "normal" vessels in an area of injury suggests that hemostatic mechanisms also play an important role in the pathogenesis of thrombosis. If we are to understand why intravascular clotting occurs and why anticoagulant therapy is of value in preventing thrombosis and its complications, it is important that we understand the mechanisms of normal blood coagulation and hemostasis. Much of our knowledge in these areas is based upon *in vitro* studies on shed blood. It is worthy of emphasis at this point that, though blood coagulation, hemostasis and thrombosis have many features in common, each may be considered a unique event occurring under specific circumstances.

THE THREE STAGES OF BLOOD COAGULATION

The development of our early knowledge of blood coagulation has been well reviewed by Biggs and Macfarlane (15), Quick (16), Jorpes (17) and Milstone (18). At the present time it is convenient to visualize blood coagulation, i.e. *fibrin formation in test tubes,* as occurring in 3 stages and requiring the successive interplay of coagulation factors. The three stages are: 1) the generation of thromboplastin; 2) the conversion of prothrombin to thrombin; and 3) the conversion of fibrinogen to fibrin. The factors and the stage in which each acts are listed in table I.

A schematic view of the interaction of these factors in each stage is presented in Figure 1. This view must not be construed as the final picture of the sequence of events in test tube coagulation (19, 20). It is useful in thinking about the phenomenon of coagula-

46

TABLE I.

FACTORS OPERATING IN THREE ARBITRARY STAGES OF COAGULATION[+],[*],[**]

The First Stage The Generation of Thromboplastin	*The Second Stage* The Conversion of Prothrombin to Thrombin	*The Third Stage* The Conversion of Fibrinogen to Fibrin
Hageman Factor	II Prothrombin	I Fibrinogen
Plasma Thromboplastin Antecedent	III Thromboplastin	Thrombin
IV Calcium	V Proaccelerin	IV Calcium
IX Plasma Thromboplastin Component	IV Calcium	Fibrin Stabilizing Factor
VIII Antihemophilic Factor	VII Proconvertin ♦	
V Proaccelerin[§]		
Stuart Factor[@]		
III Thromboplastin (platelets)		

[+] The nomenclature recommendations of the International Committee on Nomenclature of Coagulation Factors (209, 210) are used here.

[*] Some of the factors participate in more than one stage, e.g. calcium ion is operative in all three stages and factor V (proaccelerin) in the first two stages.

[**] The chemical nature of most of the factors is moderately well known: I, glycoglobulin; II, $alpha_2$ glycoglobulin; III, lipoprotein; IV, mineral; V, euglobulin; VI, protein; VII, protein; VIII, beta globulin; IX, $beta_2$ globulin; Fibrin Stabilizing Factor, probably a globulin; Hageman factor, probably a protein; plasma thromboplastin antecedent and Stuart Factor have not been well characterized.

[§] Factor VI is activated factor V. It is probably also operative in the first two stages of fibrin formation.

[@] Stuart factor has been confused with other factors, such as the Prower factor and Koller's Factor X. There is no definite evidence that the Prower factor differs from the Stuart factor, or that the Factor X of Koller is a definite entity.

[♦] Proconvertin and Stuart Factor are necessary for the activation of *tissue* thromboplastin.

tion, but relates absolutely nothing about the surface activation or the interactions of the factors, the subsequent changes in each factor, the kinetics of these reactions, the nature of the intermediates, etc. Certain aspects of these are known and will be considered in part in the following description of the three stages of coagulation.

The Generation of Plasma Thromboplastin. Platelets are a source of a potent thromboplastic material which is capable of altering prothrombin to thrombin in the presence of calcium ions and the necessary accessory factors. It takes approximately five minutes for this activated platelet material to appear as indicated by the thromboplastin or thrombin generation tests. During this five minute "lag phase," the soluble factors participating in the first stage of coagulation are reacting with the platelets and with one another (21, 22). After this, thromboplastin is produced with sudden abruptness, and, after reaching peak activity in about one minute, gradually diminishes. The anti-thromboplastin factors accounting for this decrease in activity are obscure. Thromboplastin so produced is capable of clotting recalcified plasma in eight to twelve seconds.

The "lag phase" can be shortened by the preincubation of Factor IX (plasma thromboplastin component). Surface contact with glass in some fashion alters Factor IX (plasma thromboplastin component). In consequence the platelet alteration or viscous metamorphosis (23) which is initiated by Factor VIII (anti-hemophilic factor) (24, 25) is facilitated (19), and thromboplastin generation occurs more promptly. Hageman factor, plasma thromboplastin antecedent and Stuart Factor also appear to play a role in the "lag phase," as their absence delays thromboplastin generation. Exactly how these four factors participate in the "lag phase" or platelet disruption is unclear (26). Whereas thromboplastin appearance time can be prolonged by decreasing the concentrations of these factors, it is not so influenced by decreasing the platelet numbers which results rather in a decreased thromboplastin activity. Factor V is also absorbed to the platelet surface (27) and may also play a role in platelet metamorphosis and therefore thromboplastin generation.

As the platelet disintegrates, several platelet components are released; those which are particulate have been isolated after ultra-centrifugation and one of these appears to contain the thrombo-plastic activity of the whole disrupted platelets (28). This thrombo-plastic material appears to be a phospholipoprotein (29) ; the phos-pholipid is probably phosphatidylethanolamine (30), though phos-phatidylserine has also been implicated (31).

The next step in the activation of the platelet extrusate to a thromboplastin capable of converting prothrombin to thrombin is its combination with factor V or VI (32). This aggregate is prob-ably the active plasma thromboplastin. Each stage in the generation of thromboplastin appears to require calcium ion (19). Factor VII is apparently *not* necessary in the activation of plasma thrombo-plastin (33) ; as will be shown later, it is necessary for the activation of tissue thromboplastin and apparently is linked to thromboplastin by calcium ion (34).

Chemistry of Thromboplastin. In studying the nature and mechanism of action of thromboplastin it has been found that phospholipids from brain (35), lung (36), soybean (37), eggs (38), plasma chylomicra (39), and erythrocytes (31) can sub-stitute for the platelet substance, platelet factor 3, the phospholipo-protein which is essential for normal plasma thromboplastin forma-tion. The chemical and physical characteristics common to these thromboplastic phosphatides have been partially elucidated (40, 41). Recent evidence suggests that the active lipid is phosphatidyle-thanolamine which depends for activity on its 1) unsaturated fatty acids (which facilitate its colloidal dispersion), 2) negatively charged phosphate group, and 3) amino proton donor group (30). The particle size of the phosphatidylethanolamine micelles also determines its coagulant potency (42, 43), perhaps by influencing its ability to form thromboplastic lipoprotein complexes.

Using chromatographic isolation methods and the thrombo-plastin generation test Troup and Reed (31) and Marcus and Spaet (44) found phosphatidylserine a considerably more active procoagulant than phosphatidylethanolamine; this was confirmed also by Barkhan et al. (45) using the versene anticoagulant used by Troup and Reed. However, using other anticoagulants phosphatidylserine had an anticoagulant action (46). When the results of experiments depend on the colloidal size of the test particles and the anticoagulants used, the begetting of conflicting conclusions so common to *in vitro* coagulation studies is not surprising. It thus remains to be established which phospholipids are operative in thromboplastin generation; what protein, lipid, and Ca^{++} interactions are necessary to produce an active thromboplastin; and whether this complex acts stoichiometrically (41) or enzymatically (40) in transforming prothrombin to thrombin.

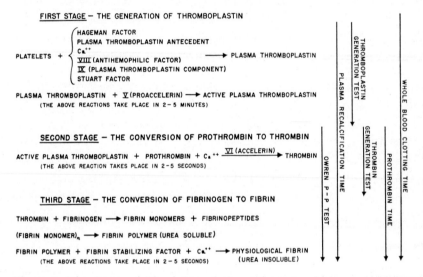

Figure 1. The Stages of Blood Coagulation. The tests which measure each stage are seen to the right of the figure. The prothrombin time test substitutes tissue thromboplastin and requires Factor VII.

The Conversion of Prothrombin to Thrombin. After the formation of the active lipoprotein thromboplastin, it reacts with prothrombin and converts this inert protein to the active enzyme, thrombin. The reaction is influenced by factors IV, V and VI.

Prothrombin is a protein containing about 3% polysaccharide (47) including glucosamine (48) and a glucose polymer (49). A few believe this polysaccharide is the antithrombin, heparin (50), which is simply released in the formation of thrombin: substantial evidence refutes this hypothesis (51). The protein fraction of prothrombin contains eighteen amino acids (52), including the sulfur containing amino acids cystine and methionine (53). The disulfide (-S-S-) linkage in cystine probably plays an important role in the activation of prothrombin, in contrast to the inactive sulfhydryl (-SH) group of methionine. Compounds which inhibit -SH groups, such as alkylating and mercaptide forming agents, are not inhibitory to the conversion of prothrombin to thrombin; whereas compounds altering disulfide linkages as by reduction (-S-S- to -SH) or sulfitolysis are all inhibitory to this conversion (54). Prothrombin contains disulfide linkages, whereas thrombin does not. This suggests that these linkages are important in the alignment of prothrombin with either thromboplastin or the accessory factors necessary for thrombin production.

Understanding of the conversion of prothrombin to thrombin is further complicated by the observation that the molecular weight of thrombin is almost the same as that of prothrombin when calculated from ultracentrifuge data (47). Supposedly loss of carbohydrate occurs during thrombin formation, but how much and what moiety, if any, replaces the carbohydrate is unknown.

The Conversion of Fibrinogen to Fibrin. There are several recent comprehensive reviews of this final phase of coagulation (55, 56, 47). The reactants of this stage in this final phase of coagulation and the stepwise changes that occur are presented at the bottom of Figure 1.

Thrombin is a proteolytic enzyme of considerable specificity for fibrinogen but does have a proteolytic action on other protein substrates (47, 57). It has amidase, esterase, and peptidase activity (47, 58). It is even capable of splitting synthetic peptide substrates such as tosylarginine methyl ester (59) by hydrolytic cleavage of the ester bond, and this esterase activity appears proportional to the thrombin activity. Thrombin splits fibrinogen molecules into a soluble fibrin and a fibrinopeptide; as a result, fibrinogen loses about 3% of its nitrogen (60), and a small amount of hexose. The peptide cleavage probably occurs at an arginyl-glycine bond (61, 62).

In the polymerization of fibrin, tyrosine is apparently important. It is one of the N-terminal amino acids of fibrinogen, and exposure of fibrinogen to tyrosinase prevents polymerization of fibrin (63). Following cleavage of the acidic peptide, the fibrino-monomers apparently lose their repelling forces or develop into more polar molecules, and by reorientation associate with one another in parallel fashion via electrostatic (64) and hydrogen bondings (65) to form the fibrin polymer. These bondings are weak as indicated by the solubility of the fibrin gel in 5M urea (66), as well as several inorganic and organic salts, weak acids and alkali. This urea-soluble fibrin polymer is then changed into what is called physiological fibrin.

Physiological fibrin is not soluble in the above reagents, and has greater mechanical strength, presumably because the fibrin is altered by the formation of additional bonds, which are probably disulphide bonds (64). Calcium ion is required for this transformation. An additional required plasma factor, "fibrin-stabilizing-factor," has now been purified (67) and apparently functions as an initiator of disulfide interchange (68).

By electron microscopy the final fibrin clot consists of a three-dimensional network of interwoven fibers. At rather regular intervals of 250 Å, the fibers contain cross-striations (regions of greatest folding), which are the sites of side by side association of the unit fibers (69). The diameter of the unit fiber is directly proportional to the pH. The fiber lengthens by end to end linkages and thickens by lateral association of the unit fibers.

The fate of an *in vitro* fibrin clot varies. It may eventually be dissolved, presumably by the action of thrombin (70) or fibrinolysin; or it may contract (syneresis), perhaps under the influence of platelet serotonin.

LIPIDS AND COAGULATION

Numerous *in vitro* experiments evaluating the influence of lipids on each stage of coagulation have demonstrated that free fatty acids and phospholipids, in contrast to triglycerides and cholesterol, have potent influences on thromboplastin or thrombin generation, and show either procoagulant or anticoagulant activity. The difficulties in these *in vitro* studies have been summarized by Silver et al. (46).

Phospholipids. Impure lipid mixtures were used in early studies of the effects of lipids on *in vitro* coagulation and largely explain the conflicting results reported (71). Paper and column chromatographic methods developed recently (72) have made available more purified phospholipid preparations (31, 44). The effect of various phospholipids depends upon the test situation (lipid solubility, addition of emulsifying or chelating agents, etc.) (46.) There is good agreement that purified phosphatidylethanolamine is important in promoting thromboplastin formation, as is phosphatidylserine in certain situations, in contrast to lecithin (73) and inositol phosphatide (74). Other inactive phospholipids are lysophosphatidylethanolamine, lysolecithin (the monostearoyl), phosphorylcholine, phosphorylserine, and ox brain acetal (75).

Thromboplastin is a lipoprotein whose active lipid component is a cephalin (36). This cephalin, phosphatidylethanolamine, can substitute for platelet or tissue thromboplastin in thrombin or thromboplastin generation tests (31, 76). Substitution of serine for ethanolamine in the phospholipid results in phosphatidylserine which has under some conditions anticoagulant properties (46) (for conflicting evidence see page 49). Phosphatidylethanolamine may react with Factors VIII, and IX (35), and subsequently with V and VII and thereby become an active thromboplastin (19).

Serum cephalins might play a role in coronary artery thrombosis. The serum phospholipids of subjects with coronary artery disease and suitable controls have been partitioned and it was found that the patients did have higher concentrations of cephalins (77). It is conceivable, but speculative, that this abundance of cephalins (presumably including phosphatidylethanolamine) may predispose to coronary artery thrombosis under certain as yet unexplained conditions.

Fatty Acids. Poole has reviewed the experiments demonstrating the influence of fatty acid chain length on the plasma recalcification time in the absence or presence of Russel's viper venom (the Stypven time) (71). Several studies have shown that the former is shortened by long chain saturated fatty acids (C_{16}-C_{20}), and the latter by shorter chain fatty acids (C_{12}) (78-80). The concentration of free fatty acid required to influence these tests is seen physiologically after a fatty meal (71).

Dietary Fat. In 1953, Fullerton et al. demonstrated that the whole blood clotting in silicone tubes and the plasma Stypven time were shortened after a fatty meal (81). Since then there has been general agreement that the plasma Stypven clotting time is shortened after a fatty meal (82), but no agreement that the plasma recalcification time (83, 84) and whole blood silicone clotting time are significantly shortened (85). The accelerated coagulation demonstrated by these tests is independent of the type of fat consumed (84, 86).

The circulating factor responsible for the accelerated plasma Stypven time following a fatty meal could not be correlated with the plasma total fatty acids or neutral fat (82). However, if chylomicra (see page 115) appearing after a fatty meal are removed by flotation, this clotting time is prolonged (87). If neutral fat or cholesterol, which make up 95% of the chylomicron weight, were added in amounts equivalent to that removed with the chylomicra, the clotting time remained prolonged. If phosphatidylethanolamine was added, the clotting was restored to normal. Other phospholipids or their hydrolytic products have so far been found to be ineffective (71). The chylomicron protein has not been similarly tested.

The plasma free fatty acids may also be responsible for the shortening of the Stypven time as they do increase after a fatty meal. They are suppressed after carbohydrate feeding (88), which interestingly enough blocks the appearance of plasma lactescence (chylomicra) and clotting acceleration after a fatty meal (89,90). The suppression of free fatty acids by carbohydrate feeding may well account for this observation.

The above *in vitro* studies have been given new emphasis by Thomas and Hartroft (91). They were able to produce coronary thrombosis and myocardial infarction, as well as renal artery thrombosis with renal infarction in the rat by *feeding* a diet high in fat, cholesterol, thiouracil and cholate.

These studies emphasize the interrelationships of diet, coagulation and thrombosis. As will be developed subsequently the influence of diet on plasma lipids is also important in the experimental production of atherosclerosis. These observations suggest that whatever relationships exist between atherosclerosis and thrombosis ultimately may be explained by their dependence upon closely related, if not identical, serum lipid elements.

HEMOSTASIS

Hemostasis may be defined as the events that occur following vascular injury which result in staunching the flow of blood. It is accomplished by the interplay of blood vessels, platelets and blood coagulation (fibrin formation), but is not necessarily dependent on the participation of all three. In fact, it *may* be adequate in the complete or partial absence of some of the coagulation factors (19): in Hageman Factor deficiency, hemostasis is virtually normal (92); dicumarol induced coagulation deficiencies may permit adequate hemostasis even at surgery (93); and even classical hemophilia (Factor VIII deficiency) presents a normal bleeding time.

Blood Vessels in Hemostasis. Bleeding from large (94) and small arteries, veins and capillaries (95-97) can be stopped by vasospasm alone. This vasoconstriction may be reinforced by serotonin, a humor elaborated by platelets and mast cells, although the importance of this humor in hemostasis has recently been questioned (98).

Vascular constriction does not persist indefinitely, but is reinforced by other factors participating in hemostasis. Capillaries may also be occluded by edema and hematoma formation which increase tissue pressure and encourage the injured sticky endothelia of the capillary walls to approximate and adhere tenaciously (16). The sticky endothelium becomes positively charged, losing its characteristic non-wettability, so that all varieties of blood elements, especially the platelets, adhere to further occlude bleeding vessels.

Platelets in Hemostasis. The platelet plays four roles in hemostasis: it **1)** plugs small vessels (95); **2)** releases a potent vasoconstrictor (serotonin) (98); **3)** contributes plasma thromboplastin and other procoagulants (99, 100); and, **4)** facilitates clot retraction (101).

Platelets, probably with the aid of thrombin, clump and form a refractile "white thrombus" plug (95). The platelet contributes four procoagulants: platelet factor 1 resembles factor V, but is particulate; platelet factor 2 accelerates thrombin conversion of fibrinogen to fibrin; platelet factor 3 has thromboplastic activity in the presence of factor V; and platelet factor 4 antagonizes the action of heparin. These factors have been isolated, but not in pure form, and are reviewed in more detail by Seegers (47) and Ackeroyd (96). Clot retraction depends on the number and quality of the platelets (101, 102), which adhere to the fibrin clot and form interlacing tentacles which subsequently contract.

Fibrin Formation in Hemostasis. Tissue injury liberates tissue thromboplastin which reacts immediately with factors V, VII, Ca^{++} and Stuart factor, inducing fibrin formation in ten to fourteen seconds. The first and most of the second stage of blood coagulation are bypassed, decreasing the time required for fibrin formation by approximately five minutes.

Fibrin then enmeshes the formed elements of the blood and occludes the ruptured vessel by the sheer bulk of the red clot. Fibrin has a high affinity for thrombin, reducing the latter's availability for additional fibrin formation (103). It also forms a scaffold for the tissue cells of repair, the macrophages and fibroblasts. In time the clot contracts and is either completely consumed by the reparative processes or dissolved by native fibrinolysins.

The mechanism of fibrin formation in hemostasis is presumptive and is derived from *in vitro* studies using platelet *or* tissue thromboplastins which are presumably both operative in hemostasis. The differences in the generation of thromboplastin from platelets and tissue are seen in Table II. A host of accessory factors are necessary for platelet thromboplastin activation. Only Factors IV, V, VII and Stuart are necessary for tissue thromboplastin activation; of these factor VII is apparently not necessary for platelet thromboplastin activation. Many of the accessory factors in platelet thromboplastin activation are operative in rupturing the platelet for thromboplastin release; tissue thromboplastin, in contrast, is almost immediately available. Thus, hemophilia, the hemophilioid disorders, and thrombocytopenia are disorders primarily of platelet thromboplastin generation. Factor V deficiency represents a disorder in both platelet and tissue thromboplastin activation and factor VII deficiency a disorder of tissue thromboplastin activation

TABLE II

CONDITIONS NECESSARY FOR THROMBOPLASTIN GENERATION DURING *in vitro* COAGULATION, HEMOSTASIS, AND THROMBOSIS

	Coagulation	*Hemostasis*	*Thrombosis*
Initiating Factors	Surface Contact	Injury	Injury; Stasis; Unknown
Thromboplastin Source	Platelets	Platelets; Tissues	Vascular Intima; Formed Elements of the Blood; Plasma Components; Unknown
Coagulation Factors for Thromboplastin: a) Liberation	Hageman and Stuart, Plasma Thromboplastin Antecedent, VIII and IX	As for Coagulation	none
b) Activation	V and Ca^{++}	IV, V, VII and Stuart	As for Hemostasis

alone. Anticoagulants of the coumarin type reduce many of the coagulation factors necessary for platelet and tissue thromboplastin generation and thereby account for the hemostatic defect seen so frequently following the chronic administration of these drugs. These effects will be discussed in greater detail in the chapter on anticoagulant therapy, but it is worthy of mention here that any clotting test which utilizes tissue thromboplastin (such as Quick's "prothrombin" test) is not a measure of most of the coagulation factors important in platelet thromboplastin generation.

Chapter III

ANTICOAGULANTS

COUMARIN AND INDANEDIONE ANTICOAGULANTS

History. In the early 1920's in North Dakota and Alberta, Canada, veterinarians were confounded by cattle dying of hemorrhage. This was ultimately found to be the result of a poisoning by some agent of spoiled sweet clover hay. Successful isolation, identification, and pharmacological evaluation of the hemorrhagic agent, bishydroxycoumarin (Dicumarol®), and its extensive clinical use for the treatment and prevention of thrombosis are history. The benefits derived and the success of the cooperative efforts of basic and applied scientists are beautifully chronicled in two excellent reviews (104, 105).

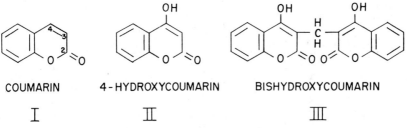

COUMARIN   4-HYDROXYCOUMARIN   BISHYDROXYCOUMARIN

I   II   III

Figure 2. Structural formulae of coumarin, 4-hydroxycoumarin, and bishydroxycoumarin (Dicoumarol®).

Coumarin (I), 4-hydroxy-coumarin (II), and bishydroxycoumarin (Dicumarol®) (III) are depicted in Figure 2. Dicumarol® is composed of two 4-hydroxy-coumarins joined by a methylene bridge. In an attempt to find safer anticoagulants and define the molecular features of bishydroxycoumarin which determine its anticoagulant activity, many derivatives have been synthesized. Those which have anticoagulant activity may be classified into three groups, examples of which are seen in Table III under A, B, and C.

TABLE III

CLINICALLY USEFUL DERIVATIVES OF COUMARIN AND INDANEDIONE

Derivatives of Coumarin	Pharmacopoeia Name	Trade Name	Structure
A. Two Coumarin Ring Compounds			
1. 3,3' methylene, bis- (4-hydroxycoumarin)	Bishydroxycoumarin	Dicumarol	R = −H
2. 3,3'-carboxymethylene bis- (4-hydroxycoumarin)	Ethylbiscoumacetate	Tromexan	R = −COOC$_2$H$_5$
B. 3-Substituted, 4-Hydroxy-coumarin			
1. 3- (αphenyl--acetyl ethyl) -4-hydroxycoumarin	Warfarin	Coumadin	R = −CH (CH$_2$−CO−CH$_3$) (phenyl)
2. 3- (1'-phenyl-propyl-) 4-hydroxycoumarin	Phenprocoumon	Marcoumar	R = −CH (CH$_2$−CH$_3$) (phenyl)
3. 3- (α-acetonyl-4-nitro-benzyl) -4-hydroxycoumarin	Acenocoumarin	Sintrom	R = −CH (CH$_2$−CO−CH$_3$) (phenyl-NO$_2$)
C. Cyclic Acetal Derivative of 4-Hydroxycoumarin			
1. 3,4- (2'-methyl-2'-methoxy-4'-phenyl) dihydropyrano coumarin	Cyclocoumarol	Cumopyran	R$_1$ = (phenyl); R$_2$ = −CH$_3$; R$_3$ = −CH$_3$
Derivatives of 1:3 Indanedione			
1. 2-phenyl-1,3-indanedione	Phenylindanedione	Hedulin	R = (phenyl)
2. 2-diphenylacetyl-1,3-indanedione	Diphenadione	Dipaxin	R = −CH$_2$−O−C(H)(phenyl)(phenyl)
3. 2-p-anisyl indanedione	Anisindione	Miradon	R = (phenyl)OCH$_3$

Another related group of compounds, the indanedione anti-coagulants, was described by Kabat, et al. (106). Subsequently several additional derivatives were tested, examples of which are shown in Table III.

Molecular Structure and Anticoagulant Activity. Attempts have been made to correlate the anticoagulant activity of these compounds with their molecular structure (104, 107). Stahmann et al. (108) found that the anticoagulant activity was not confined to 4-hydroxycoumarin. Three substituted 4-hydroxycoumarins were also active, aryl groups imparting greater activity than alkyl groups (Table III B). Knoblach et al. (cited in 107) believed that the active form of most of these anticoagulant drugs was the 2-hydroxy tautomer (2-hydroxychromone, IV) of 4-hydroxy-coumarin (II) (see Figure 4). But Mentzer postulated that the

$$\begin{matrix} O & R & OH \\ \| & | & | \\ -C- & C= & C- \end{matrix}$$ grouping of the lactone ring is responsible for activity

(109) as even some vitamin K derivatives with this grouping have *anticoagulant* activity. If **R** is of a chain length less than C_5, vitamin K activity is favored; if **R** is greater than C_5, the vitamin K preparation has anticoagulant activity. However, there are exceptions to this rule for some derivatives are completely inactive. Molecular alterations influence the solubility, absorption, and metabolism of these compounds thus complicating precise delineation of the substituents and molecular configurations that are important in anticoagulant action.

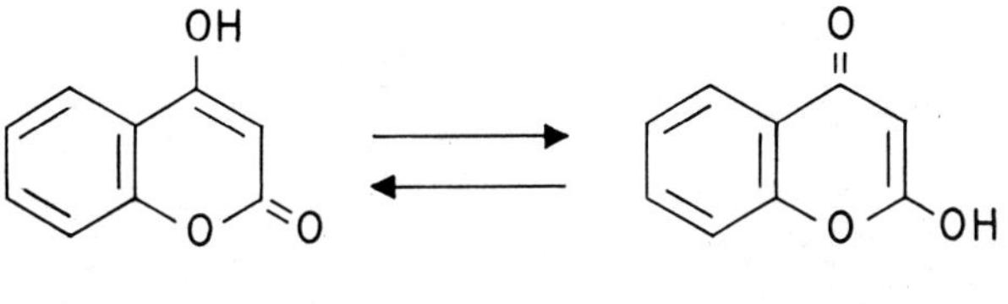

4 - HYDROXYCOUMARIN   2 - HYDROXYCHROMONE

II   IV

Figure 3. The conversion of 4-hydroxycoumarin to its tautomer 2-hydroxy-chromone (see text for details).

Mechanism of Action of Dicumarol. Dicumarol® inhibits the synthesis of several coagulation proteins which are manufactured in the liver (110). It is ordinarily assumed that other coumarin and indanedione derivatives produce their pharmacological effects in a similar manner. Factor VII (proconvertin) and, to a slightly lesser extent, prothrombin are reduced *early* in therapy. Stuart factor, Factor IX (Christmas Factor) and plasma thromboplastin antecedent (110) are reduced after *prolonged* therapy. Factor V (Proaccelerin) is slightly reduced early, returns to normal and remains so, except in severe intoxication, when it, as well as prothrombin, may all but disappear. Factor VIII (Antihemophilic factor), believed to be synthesized in the extrahepatic reticuloendothelial system, Hageman factor and fibrinogen are not affected. The inhibition of protein synthesis which Dicumarol® induces is temporary, and is usually relieved in a few days when Dicumarol® administration ceases, or vitamin K is exhibited.

The mechanism by which Dicumarol® inhibits protein synthesis is still hypothetical. It was early thought that Dicumarol® operated by competitive inhibition of vitamin K_1, because of their similar structure and the ability of vitamin K_1 to reverse the pharmacologic effects of Dicumarol®. Further support resided in the facts that vitamin K_1-like quinones have been found in lipid extracts of liver mitochondria (and microsomes), sites of protein synthesis in the liver, and vitamin K_1 is necessary for efficient mitochondrial oxidative phosphorylation upon which the synthesis of peptides depend (111). Oxidative phosphorylation, i.e., the synthesis of adenosinetriphosphate (ATP) by mitochondria, requires adenosinediphosphate (ADP) and inorganic phosphate (P_i) and is apparently "coupled" to the oxidation of reduced diphosphopyridine nucleotide (DPNH) (112). In this reaction,

$$DPNH + H^+ + \tfrac{1}{2}O_2 + 3\ ADP + 3P_i \rightleftharpoons DPN^+ + H_2O + 3ATP \quad [1];$$

a pair of electrons from DPNH are transferred to oxygen by a chain of liver cell enzymes, called the electron transfer system. During this electron transfer, three molecules of ADP are mysteriously phosphorylated to three molecules of ATP, at several places along the electron transfer chain. Thus, the phosphorylation of ADP to ATP is said to be "coupled" to the oxidation of DPNH via the electron transfer system.

As Dicumarol® interferes with the efficiency of ATP synthesis and does not interfere with oxidation of DPNH, Dicumarol® was thought to divorce the synthesis of ATP from the electron transfer system. More recent evidence indicates that Dicumarol® may, in addition, interfere directly with the phosphorylation of ADP, and vitamin K_1 may have a role here as well as in the electron transfer system (113, 114). The final assignment of the mechanism of action of Dicumarol® will probably have to await definition of a precise role for vitamin K_1 in electron transport and oxidative phosphorylation (115).

Metabolism. Bishydroxycoumarin (116, 117), ethylbiscoumacetate (118, 119), phenylindanedione (120, 121) and warfarin (122) are the most extensively studied anticoagulants (123). As there is considerable species variability, our comments will be confined to the metabolism of these compounds in man. These anticoagulants are usually completely absorbed; in a minority of individuals, and in some with diarrhea, absorption may be incomplete. Except for a minor loss of the unchanged anticoagulant to the urine, these anticoagulants appear to undergo transformation prior to excretion. The fate of the absorbed anticoagulants is reasonably well known except for the nature of the metabolic end products.

Ethylbiscoumacetate (Tromexan®) is rapidly and completely absorbed into the portal circulation, enters the liver where it presumably exerts its pharmacologic effect and is converted to hydroxytromexan. The latter is a metabolite devoid of anticoagulant activity which is excreted via the bile, whence it may be reabsorbed, and excreted via the kidneys. The absorption, metabolism and excretion of this most rapidly effective oral anticoagulant is so fast that virtually all the ethylbiscoumacetate is excreted before the peak reduction of the plasma prothrombin activity becomes apparent (24 hours). The reduction is short lived as the Quick prothrombin time returns to normal in two days. Of great interest is the report of the uricosuric action of ethylbiscoumacetate (124), suggesting that the anticoagulants may have other metabolic effects.

Phenylindanedione (Hedulin®) is somewhat longer acting. It circulates in both erythrocytes and plasma, where it is detectable in from one to thirty-six hours after administration, with a peak level at two to three hours. The peak prolongation of the Quick prothrombin time occurs about 48 hours after administration, a measurable effect lasting up to four days. Phenylindanedione and some of its metabolites are red in alkaline urine.

Bishydroxycoumarin (Dicumarol®) is also usually completely absorbed. It was at first thought that, because of the ease with which Dicumarol® is converted to salicylic acid by chemical means, the latter was the active metabolite. However, aspirin is a very weak depressant of prothrombin activity and salicylic acid is not found as an urinary metabolite of Dicumarol® (104). Dicumarol® circulates in plasma bound to protein (probably albumin and perhaps some globulins), which no doubt accounts for its prolonged appearance in plasma (up to 9 days) and its absence from both urine and cerebrospinal fluid. In some subjects with rapid metabolism plasma Dicumarol® is undetectable after two days. The plasma level does not correlate with plasma prothrombin activity; for example, the peak prolongation of the Quick prothrombin time occurs twenty-four to thirty-six hours *after* the peak plasma level, which varies from two to twenty-four hours depending upon the dose. Maximum prolongation persists about twenty-four hours, gradually returning to normal in five to seven days.

Warfarin Sodium (Coumadin®) is also completely absorbed, but has the advantage that it may be used parenterally. It is reportedly possible to reduce prothrombin activity to "therapeutic levels" in eighteen to twenty-four hours, but in practice this often requires forty-eight hours. After a priming dose, prothrombin activity returns to control levels in five to seven days. Little is known of the metabolism of warfarin sodium.

Toxicity. The major toxic effect is hemorrhage. Hemorrhage is caused by alteration of the coagulation factors involved in the first two stages of coagulation, and an as yet unproven effect on the capillary vasculature which is noted after Dicumarol® intoxication to be widely dilated (125). Additional evidence of a capillary defect are the purpura, hematuria and melena seen not infrequently even when the Quick prothrombin test may be within the therapeutic range. In order of preference the four methods for the control of bleeding attendant therapy with coumarin or indanedione compounds are the temporary withdrawal of the anticoagulants, local hemostatics, vitamin K_1, and blood transfusions. Owren believes major hemorrhage can be reduced to a minor figure by meticulously measuring the effect upon factor VII and prothrombin concentration as a guide to control of anticoagulant therapy. While this objective is desirable, it is doubtful that this has been accomplished by any laboratory test in use today (see page 58). Other side reactions are rare. Varieties of reaction reported include necrosing cutaneous hemorrhages (126), and alopecia from coumarin derivatives (127); and agranulocytosis, liver toxicity and scarlatiniform eruption (128) from phenylindanedione.

Clinical Comparison of Oral Anticoagulants. It is the authors' experience that all oral anticoagulants are difficult to administer. While ethylbiscoumacetate might be useful for rapid prolongation of the Quick prothrombin time, there is no substitute for the immediacy of the heparin effect, and the vicissitudes of ethylbiscoumacetate therapy do not recommend it. Because of the toxicity of phenylindanedione, bishydroxycoumarin and warfarin sodium are at present the drugs of choice for long term anticoagulant therapy. As is the case with digitalis derivatives, the chief differences among these preparations are seen in their speed of onset and duration of action, and in the disparity between plasma level of the drug and their biological activity. While the rapid acting drug affords more rapid control of hemorrhage on withdrawal, it also permits wider fluctuation in prothrombin activity with long term use.

HEPARIN

In the course of trying to isolate a thromboplastic substance from liver, Maclean in 1916 isolated an impure anticoagulant substance from the heart and liver (129). This material was purified and named heparin to indicate its derivation from liver (130). Heparin was subsequently found in other body tissues (131). It was further purified in 1936 (132) and its effective clinical use for the treatment of thrombosis was first reported in 1937 (133, 134).

Source. Heparin is isolated by precipitation with barium from tissue extracts of domestic mammals, preferably bovine lung and liver (132). Mast cells appear to be the source of heparin and the heparin content of a tissue parallels its mast cell count, e g., rat liver is sparse in mast cells and low in heparin, whereas rat skin is rich in mast cells and high in heparin (131). Mast cells extrude granules which stain metachromatically for heparin with toluidine blue. The biological and staining properties of heparins isolated from different animal sources or from different organs of the same animal vary, and indicate that heparin is not a single compound (135). For example, heparins from different sources have different anticoagulant potency and may not be homogeneous as indicated in paper chromatographic systems. Anticoagulant activity, protein combining ability, and metachromatic activity are all thought to be related to the number of sulfuric acid substituents, yet beef and dog heparin, though equal in this regard, have different anticoagulant activity. Furthermore, there is evidence that such heparins may vary also in elemental analysis, molecular size (136), metachromatic properties, protein combining power, solubility properties and lability to hydrolysis (135). The clinician must keep these variations in mind for such differences may explain the conflicting reports on the clinical efficacy of heparin.

Chemistry. The hydrolysis of heparin yields glucosamine, d-glucuronic acid (137) and sulfuric acid (138). These hydrolytic residues appear to be linked together to form tetrasaccharide units (139) (Figure 5). Since the *average* molecular weight of heparin is about 20,000, the tetrasaccharide units must be highly polymerized (140). Glucosamine and d-glucuronic acid units are linked in alternate fashion and when esterified with sulfuric acid

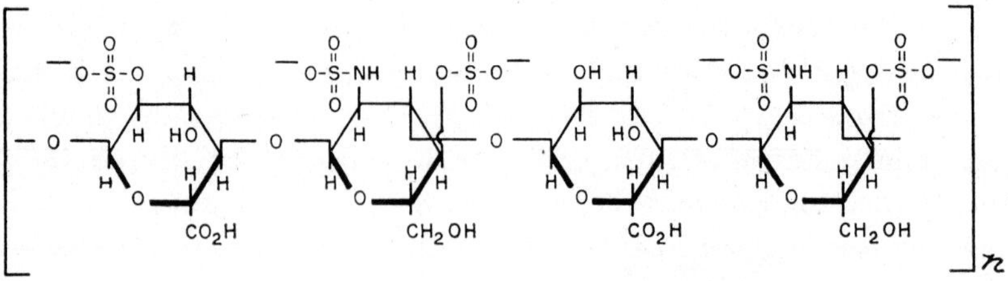

A TETRASACCHARIDE UNIT OF HEPARIN

Figure 4. Structural formula of the basic unit of heparin, demonstrating the numerous sites of electronegativity.

result in the strongest organic acid in the animal body (140), with a high electronegative charge (141). The sulfuric acid is in sulfamide linkage in glucosamine; the resulting glucosulfamine is dextrorotatory (142). Heparin containing this compound is also dextrorotatory and is called *alpha-heparin* (136). Another sulfated amino-polysaccharide (monosulfuric acid), which is levorotatory because it contains l-acetyl glucosamine, has been isolated from heparin-containing extracts of beef and sheep lung. It is called *beta-heparin* and has many properties of alpha heparin (135).

Heparin is associated with a lipoprotein in nature (143) and is a coprecipitant in the isolation of trypsin and chrymotrypsin. This suggests that, by acting as a strong protein acceptor, its anticoagulant effect is accomplished by the inactivation of enzymes and proteins participating in blood coagulation. The chemistry of heparin has been reviewed by Foster and Huggard (144).

The Anticoagulant Activity of Heparin. Heparin functions as an anticoagulant in several ways: 1) it acts as an antithrombin (if a serum cofactor is present (145)) and facilitates the absorption of thrombin by fibrin (146); 2) it inhibits thromboplastin generation by inhibiting Factor VIII (147); 3) it decreases platelet adhesiveness (148); and 4) it can neutralize other plasma procoagulants such as Factor V (149). It may also contribute to the maintenance of an electronegative charge on the endothelial lining of blood vessels. The serum cofactor for heparin antithrombin effect has not been definitely isolated, but is associated with the albumin fraction. The lipo-protein with which heparin is associated, after isolation from mast cells, manifests cofactor activity (149). Chargaff, et al. (150) demonstrated that when heparin combined with lung thromboplastin a lipid is released which may be an active anticoagulant (151).

In addition to its anticoagulant effect, heparin inhibits numerous enzymes, is antimetabolic *in vitro,* forms insoluble heparin-protein salts under special circumstances, and is an anticomplement (136). Its role in activating lipoprotein lipase or clearing factor will be reviewed in the last section.

Metabolism. After intravenous heparin injection, there is a lag of about three minutes before an anticoagulant effect is noted, which is presumably due to the protein-heparin combination time. The rate of disappearance of heparin from the circulation is exponential, so that high levels of heparin cannot be maintained for long after a single intravenous injection.

Unchanged heparin is in part excreted in the urine. The heparin metabolite excreted in the urine is metachromatic to toluidine blue or Azure A dye derived from toluidine blue, but has no anticoagulant activity. It is called uroheparin but is, by chromatographic criteria, at least two compounds of unknown nature (135). The site of heparin conversion to uroheparin is unknown.

An enzyme, "heparinase," capable of altering the anticoagulant and metachromatic activity of heparin was isolated from the rabbit liver (152) and on purification appears to be a non-specific sulfatase (135). Such enzymatic activity has been demonstrated in extracts of liver from many species excepting the dog. As most of the heparin is not excreted in the urine and disappears rapidly from the blood stream, it has been assumed that heparinase may be responsible for inactivating heparin.

Antiheparins. Protamine, administered slowly and intravenously, will neutralize an equivalent amount of heparin rather promptly; in excess it has an anticoagulant effect. Toluidine blue may be used as an heparin antidote but its effect is less predictable, and the dosage required is three to four times that of protamine. These drugs may precipitate hypotension, bradycardia and dyspnea when given in excess; and methemoglobinemia has been reported from toluidine blue administration.

A new antiheparin agent, a polymer, hexadimethrene bromide (Polybrene®), which is a synthetic quaternary ammonium salt, has been found effective in neutralizing heparin still more rapidly (5 minutes). It neutralizes 70% its own weight of heparin and is reported not to have a coagulant effect when given in excess. Like the other antiheparins, it is effective *in vivo* and *in vitro*, but no significant toxicity has been observed (153). The rapid neutralization of heparin which is possible with these basic compounds suggests that the binding of heparin with the protein procoagulants is of a weak variety; the nature of the polysaccharide-protein interaction is obscure.

Heparinoids. Many inert polysaccharides after sulfation behave like heparin, even to the extent of being neutralized by antiheparin agents. In all instances the anticoagulant activity is less than heparin (milligram for milligram), although other effects may be greater. Several of these sulfated polysaccharides have found clinical use but appear to have no advantage over heparin. They include: alginic acid (154), pectin (155), xylan (156) and dextran sulfates (157).

The clinical toxicity of these compounds exceeds that of heparin. Alopecia and diarrhea have been reported in man. Lethal doses in the dog induce liver, intestine and kidney degenerative and inflammatory changes, without evidence of hemorrhage (158).

Clinical Considerations. Because of its rapid excretion from the blood stream following intermittent intravenous injection, measures of administration that will maintain a coagulation time prolonged two to three times normal are more economical and include intramuscular or subcutaneous injection and slow intravenous infusion. Oral heparin is not effective as an anticoagulant (159). Pain, ecchymoses, and nodules commonly occur at the injection site. Anaphylactic shock has been reported, and, while quite rare, is probably most likely to occur following rapid intravenous injection (160). Hemorrhage is unusual, and is rare if the clotting times are observed as recommended; when it occurs, antiheparins and fresh blood transfusions give prompt reversal of the bleeding tendency. Aside from differences in route of administration, heparin appears to differ from oral anticoagulants in the infrequency with which it produces significant hemorrhage. This is thought to be due to its lack of influence on the hemostatic factors impaired by the coumarin and indanedione derivatives, but may equally well be explained by its rapid metabolism and the limited experience in its long term use.

Chapter IV

THROMBOLYSIS

WITH PARTICULAR REFERENCE TO THE HUMAN FIBRINOLYSIN, PLASMIN

Anticoagulants are useful mainly in preventing further thrombotic episodes, but as these drugs have no effect in reducing the size of the original thrombus, they reduce the initial area of infarction very little if at all. Relieving the obstruction by means of the rapid dissolution of thrombi could theoretically prevent or at least reduce the size of the infarcted area. To this end fibrin digesting (thrombolytic) enzymes have been used in recent years in several clinical trials. Some of these enzymes, especially the fibrinolysins, show sufficient promise that an understanding of the human fibrinolysin system has become worthy of the general attention of physicians (161).

Following the clotting of whole blood or recalcified plasma in glass tubes, nothing beyond clot retraction can be observed. However, when similar clots are observed after collection from subjects previously stressed or treated with certain drugs, the clot is observed to liquefy with variable but measurable rapidity (162). The agent in plasma responsible for this irreversible lysis of fibrin is a euglobulin called fibrinolysin. In man this fibrinolysin is called *plasmin*.

The observation that subjects must be treated in a variety of ways to demonstrate plasmin and that globulins inhibit it suggest that plasmin normally circulates in an inactive form called plasminogen.

PLASMINOGEN

The Nature of Plasminogen. The purest isolate of this euglobulin contains considerable impurities (161, 163), but it appears to be a glycoprotein containing about 1% hexose, part of which is lost during the activation of plasminogen (164). To date it has not been possible to isolate fibrinogen free of plasminogen because of the

Thrombolysis 71

strong affinity between the two. There is likewise a strong affinity between fibrin and plasminogen, the latter being found in all fibrin clots (165, 166). This is a very important observation for, if an activator can perfuse a thrombus to activate plasminogen to plasmin, dissolution of the thrombus might obtain.

TABLE IV
ACTIVATORS OF FIBRINOLYTIC ACTIVITY*

I. *In Vivo* Activation
  A. Stress
    1. Traumatic Asphyxic Death   5. Surgery
    2. Electric Shock   6. Anxiety
    3. Tourniquet Shock   7. Hypnosis
    4. Anaphylactic Shock   8. Exercise
  B. Drugs
    1. Adrenaline   5. Protamine Sulfate
    2. Acetylcholine   6. Bacterial Pyrogens
    3. Novocain   7. Plasmin
    4. Phenylbutazone   8. Streptokinase
        9. Staphylokinase

II. *In Vitro* Activation
  A. Organic Solvents
    1. Glycerol
    2. Chloroform
  B. Tissues
  C. Body Fluids

* (161,181)

Plasminogen Activators. The activation of this fibrinolysin system can occur spontaneously, i.e., if plasminogen is exposed to glycerol buffers, it will completely activate autocatalytically to plasmin (167). The conversion of plasminogen to plasmin can be provoked by diverse means, some of which are listed in Table IV, and, many of which, appear to be mediated via the humors of the autonomic nervous system and adrenal medulla (8, 168).

Numerous tissues have a high content of particulate activator substances, *lysokinases* (169), which are not well characterized chemically but recently have been solubilized in KSCN (170) and appear thermostable especially at acid pH. The presence of an activator in tissue cultures has also been described (171).

The body fluids are also well supplied with plasminogen activators. Normal plasma contains a small amount (172) which is increased following anoxemia (173), amniotic fluid embolism (174), electroshock, etc.; the nature of this plasma activator is unknown.

Plasminogen activators have also been found in saliva (175), tears (176), milk (177) and seminal fluid (178). The activator in urine is called *urokinase* (179) and is a colorless proteolytic enzyme of considerable pH- and thermo-stability (180).

The Mechanism of Plasminogen Activation. The present understanding of the manner in which activator substances convert plasminogen to plasmin comes from our understanding of one such activator, streptokinase, an enzyme isolated from the cell free exudates of cultures of streptococcus of Lancefield Group C (H46A) (182). Commercially available streptokinase (Varidase®) is contaminated with streptodornase, a nucleoproteinase. Though a biophysically pure streptokinase has been prepared, it is not immunologically pure. Only Varidase® has seen much use clinically.

Streptokinase appears to activate plasminogen indirectly. Streptokinase stoichiometrically combines with a proactivator to form an activator, which then reacts with the plasminogen to produce plasmin, liberating the hexose and 17% of the plasminogen amino nitrogen. The evidence for an intermediate reaction involving a proactivator is found in the observation that streptokinase activates human plasminogen in contrast to that of other species; the addition of a small amount of human serum to inactive serum permits the activation of the latter's plasminogen by streptokinase (183). The nature of the proactivator is unknown but there is recent evidence that it may simply be human plasminogen.

PLASMIN

This active, stable euglobulin frequently contaminates fibrinogen fractions. Its molecular weight varies from 108,000 to 125,000 (164), and its concentration is estimated at about .001% of the plasma proteins. This potent proteolytic enzyme can inactivate coagulation factors I (fibrinogen), II (prothrombin), V (proaccelerin), VII (proconvertin), VIII (antihemophilic factor), and fibrin; and can also inactivate complement, liquefy casein and gelatin, and hydrolyze protein hormones including adrenocorticotrophin, somatotrophin and glucagon. The pathological implications of such a gamut of proteolytic activity are provocative; this proteolytic activity may explain the etiology of some hemorrhages, but especially provocative is the speculation that both nitrogen balance and protein hormone imbalance might be affected by the proteolytic activity of plasmin.

Inhibitors of Plasmin. The presence of antiactivators has been suspected but not confirmed. Assays of the antiplasmins have proven technically difficult, but these substances appear to reside in the alpha$_2$ globulin of serum (184). The antiplasmin activity of plasma substantially exceeds the potential plasmin activity (cited in 16) although this relationship may change considerably in various disease states (185). There is considerable uncertainty in this area and more than one such inhibitor may be present.

The Possible Physiological Significance of Plasmin. Any attempt to define a role for fibrinolysis is premature, but it is conceivably important in wound repair by facilitating recanalization of thrombosed vessels, and removing excess fibrin deposits. Its presence in urine, milk, tears and saliva *suggests* it may serve to prevent obstruction of the ducts of the glands secreting these body fluids when they are inflamed and filled with fibrin.

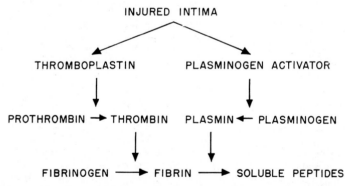

Figure 5. A proposed scheme for hemostatic balance (after Astrup).

More speculative is the implication of fibrinolysis in the maintenance of the hypothetical hemostatic balance between the continuous production and dissolution of fibrin within the vascular system (186) (see Figure 5). It is postulated that vessel wall injury is continuously occurring and results in the release of thromboplastic substances which induce local fibrinous deposits on the injured intimal surface. The chief support for this hypothesis is the rapid turnover of fibrinogen (6 days), platelets (few to 8 days), and other coagulation factors which is explained by their rapid consumption in fibrin formation; the speculation continues that fibrin "normally" coats the vessel endothelial surface and is necessary to prevent spontaneous bleeding. The lack of extensive accumulation of fibrin is explained by the continuous activation of fibrinolysin.

DIET

Inhibition of *In Vitro* Fibrinolysis. There are several methods of measuring the fibrinolysin potential of plasma (187). Fibrinolytic activity is reduced in man following fatty meals (188), and in rabbits fed cholesterol (189). The chylomicra have been implicated in this antifibrinolysin effect of fatty meals which can be reversed by carbohydrate feeding or exercise (190). Rats on a thrombogenic diet have reduced clotting times (thromboelastographic) and the time for clot lysis is prolonged (191). We have yet to learn the role fibrinolysis plays in normal physiology, and extrapolations of observations on diet-induced alterations of fibrin clot lysis in test tubes to thrombogenesis or arteriosclerosis (186) are considered premature. Nevertheless, it is certainly interesting that the low density fatty globules, the chylomicra, which increase in the blood after a fatty meal both increase the coagulant tendency and inhibit fibrinolytic activity of the blood.

THERAPEUTIC APPLICATION

The possibility of lysing thrombi *in vivo* was suggested in 1952 by Johnson and Tillet who showed that intravascular clots, artificially produced in rabbits, could be lysed by the intravenous administration of streptokinase; the therapeutic feasibility is additionally enhanced by the strong affinity between fibrin and plasminogen. Thus, if a circulating fibrinolysin were introduced into the circulation, or, if an activator of fibrin-bound-plasminogen were forced to diffuse into the clot, thrombolysis might be achieved.

The therapeutic trials used to date involve the activation of the circulating plasminogen with either intravenous infusions of streptokinase (192), or protein-free bacterial pyrogens (181), and the infusion of human plasmin (193) previously activated by streptokinase. These infusions, though showing great promise, have many disadvantages. All subjects do not develop fibrinolytic responses to streptokinase infusions; this resistance may be dose-dependent or the reflection of circulating antibody consequent to a recent strepto-coccal infection. The side effects to streptokinase, pyrogen or plas-min-streptokinase infusions are not minor and in some patients may have contributed to premature fatality. There is hope that reac-tions to the latter may be minimized, for preparations of plasmin less contaminated with streptokinase show fewer adverse side-effects (194). Proponents of this new therapy have wisely bridled their en-thusiasm, but the well founded rationale of this approach and thera-peutic gain to date are sufficiently encouraging to warrant the cautious optimism that during the next five years, fibrinolysins may become a significant addition to our therapeutic arsenal.

Chapter V

ANTICOAGULANT THERAPY FOR
MYOCARDIAL INFARCTION

THROMBOTIC COMPLICATIONS AND THE
ACUTE INFARCT

THROUGH MYOCARDIAL infarction may result from prolonged coronary insufficiency of various causes, the most common cause of infarction is coronary artery occlusion, and the incidence of thrombotic occlusion among patients dying of myocardial infarction is as high as 75% (4). Endocardial injury is common in myocardial infarction and is the site of thrombus formation in 63% of cases seen at autopsy. These mural thrombi are the sites from which thromboemboli may arise, and thromboembolism occurred in 44% of such autopsies. Clinical evidence of thromboembolism following acute myocardial infarction is about half as frequent (26%). Retrograde propagation of a coronary thrombus may occur, resulting in occlusion of a more proximal branch of the coronary artery and extending the area of infarction clinically in about 10% of cases, but at post-mortem examination, in 27%. The overall mortality in the first month following acute myocardial infarction is about 20%.

Efficacy. The results of twenty investigations collated by Wright et al. (4), including more than 5000 cases of acute myocardial infarction, indicate that the incidence of mortality and thromboembolism are cut in half by anticoagulant therapy and the incidence of extensions of the original infarctions is reduced by two-thirds. This benefit probably derives from the following known effects of anticoagulants: mural thrombi are one-half as frequent (4); recanalization of thrombosed vessels is facilitated, at least in the experimental animal (195, 196); clot propagation (197) and platelet adhesiveness are reduced.

Though there are essays critical of the efficacy of anticoagulant therapy for acute myocardial infarction (198), the evidence is over-

76

whelming that, dangerous as this therapy is, it reduces thromboembolic complications in these patients by two-thirds, and saves
half of those expected to die (4). The has convinced most major
medical centers in this country that anticoagulant therapy during
the first month or so following myocardial infarction is worthwhile.
There is less general agreement that such therapy should be continued for a period of years, perhaps indefinitely, to prevent a recurrent myocardial infarction, the commonest late sequela of this
disease. The difficulties in final evaluation of the effects of anticoagulants on the clinical course of myocardial infarction have been
described in an excellent critical essay by Gilchrist and Tulloch
(199).

LONG TERM ANTICOAGULANT THERAPY:
THE PREVENTION OF REINFARCTION

Half of the survivors of an acute myocardial infarction are dead
within five years (200). The causes of death in various series include: a new infarct in 30 to 65%, sudden and unexplained death
in 10 to 35%, and heart failure in 15 to 40%. Thromboembolism
may occur in 0 to 15%, and is not an infrequent cause of death.
This dismal outlook, and the high incidence of recurrent thrombosis, provide the rationale for the long term anticoagulant treatment of patients who have suffered myocardial infarction.

**Long Term Anticogulant Therapy at the University of Chi-
cago Clinics.** Two previous communications from this institution precede this report (201, 202). In the first, the numerous
problems arising from our experience with such therapy were reviewed; in the second, the apparent beneficial results of long term
anticoagulant therapy in 213 patients were reported without the
benefit of a control series. This is a preliminary report of the fate
of 608 patients treated for acute myocardial infarction from 1946 to
1956, and followed for at least two years, or until death, or the end
of the follow-up period. A more detailed report will be published
in full elsewhere.

Of the 608 patients, seven (1.15%) were dropped because of
complicating diagnoses of either tuberculosis or carcinoma. Nine-
teen patients (3.12%) could not be traced. Of the remaining 582

patients in whom a clinical diagnosis of acute myocardial infarction was substantiated by serial electrocardiograms, ninety-nine patients (16.2%) died during hospitalization. Four hundred and eighty-three patients survived to leave the hospital: anticoagulant therapy was discontinued in 281 of these patients, who represent the control group; 202 patients continued anticoagulant therapy returning to the laboratory for 'prothrombin time' testing as prearranged.

TABLE V

THE DISTRIBUTION OF THE AGE AND SEX IN 483 SURVIVORS OF
ACUTE MYOCARDIAL INFARCTION

	Sex	Number	Age in Years Average	Range
Controls	Male	198 (70.5%)	56.0	23-83
	Female	83 (29.5%)	58.7	32-89
Treated	Male	153 (75.7%)	55.8	32-76
	Female	49 (24.3%)	56.9	34-79

The choice of recommending long term anticoagulant therapy or not was the prerogative of the attending physician. The similarities in the sex and age distribution, seen in Table V, indicate that in *these* regards the selection was random. However, this was not the case in other aspects for in this series a patient suffering a recurrent myocardial infarction was more likely to receive long term anticoagulant therapy, than one suffering a first attack. The fate of these 483 survivors of myocardial infarction during the first two years will be reviewed here.

Results. The results of this retrospective study are recorded in Table VI. Here deaths and complications are tabulated and reveal that the group receiving anticoagulant therapy derive unequivocal benefit by virtue of a reduction in both morbidity and mortality during the first year of treatment.

In the first six months the group receiving anticoagulant therapy enjoy a highly significant reduction in the incidence of *proven myocardial infarctions* from 8.9% to 1.9%. The *cardiovascular deaths,* including reductions in deaths from myocardial infarction and sudden and unexplained deaths, were reduced in the treated group from 8.2 to 4.4%.

In the period six to twelve months after the original infarction, a somewhat altered pattern of protection is observed. The group receiving anticoagulant drugs benefitted from a highly significant reduction in cardiovascular deaths, especially of the sudden and unexplained variety. Paradoxically there was no apparent reduction in recurrent infarction and the incidence of proven reinfarction in the group was even slightly greater than in the control group (4.7% and 2.9%, respectively).

TABLE VI
The Results of Long-Term Anticoagulant Therapy Following
Acute Myocardial Infarction
— University of Chicago Study —

Period of Observation	First Six Months		Second Six Months	
	Control	Treated	Control	Treated
Number Starting Study	281	201	247	152
Number Dropped from Study or Follow-up Ended for Reasons other than Death	12	42	4	24
Number Followed for the Entire Period of Observation	269	159	243	128
	Percentage of those Followed			
Total Cardiovascular Deaths	8.2	4.4	8.6	1.6*
—From Myocardial Infarction	2.6	1.3	0.8	0.8
—Sudden and Unexplained	5.2	3.1	7.0	0*
—Thromboembolic (non-coronary)	0.4	0	0	0
—Congestive Heart Failure	0	0	0.8	0
—Hemorrhage	0	0	0	0.8
Non-Cardiovascular Deaths	0	0	0.4	0
Total Thromboembolic Episodes				
—Proven	9.3	1.9*	5.8	5.5
—Proven and Suspected+	14.5	5.0	12.8	5.5
—Excepting Myocardial Infarction	0.4	0	2.9	0.8
—All Myocardial Infarctions Deaths and Survivals	8.9	1.9*	2.9	4.7
—Suspected Coronary Thrombosis (Sudden and Unevplained Deaths)	5.2	3.1	7.0	0*
Total Survivors	91.8	95.5	90.9	98.4*
—Survivors *Free* of Thromboemboli	85.5	94.9*	86.0	93.8*

+ Suspected includes sudden and unexplained deaths.
*Significantly different from the control group by the Chi-Spuare Test, p<0.05.

Though the data are not detailed in Table VI, cardiovascular deaths during the second year are still fewer in the treated group (3.2%) than the control (6.9%). These data are incorporated in Table VII where the total two year experience is compared with other similar studies. The numbers of treated patients followed for more than two years are presently too small to permit meaningful analysis.

At the bottom of Table VI, it can be seen that a patient receiving anticoagulant drugs during the first year following a myocardial infarction is more likely to survive without the tabulated cardiovascular complications than the patients not receiving these drugs, and during the period six to twelve months after infarction is more likely to survive even if suffering a cardiovascular complication.

If the data of the two year observation period are expressed differently, either as the percentage of the number *starting* the study who suffer a given complication or as the incidence of a given complication per patient-year of observation, the reduction in recurrent myocardial infarctions and cardiovascular deaths is still evident. Furthermore, if twenty-two control patients, who suffered thromboemboli for which they subsequently received anticoagulants, are added to the treated group as they were dropped from the control group (this weighs heavily against the treated group), the benefit derived from anticoagulants is still apparent.

The authors believe that, even though admitted disadvantages exist, it is possible to derive valid conclusions from a large retrospective study of the long term benefit of anticoagulant therapy. This is possible only if whatever bias is introduced in comparing treated and control groups weighs against the former. As mentioned earlier, the treated group includes more reinfarct patients than the control group. In addition, the number of complications which are known to have occurred in the treated group are more accurately recorded than for the control group. Hence, in this study the biases *against* the treated group are many, but in the opinion of the authors give greater credence to the beneficial results accruing to the patients receiving anticoagulant drugs. This implies without proving that this benefit is attributable to the anticoagulant therapy rather than merely to the more close observation which accompanies such therapy.

Comparable Studies. Five other studies of the effect of long term anticoagulant therapy are of sufficient size, duration and control to warrant conclusions about the efficacy of anticoagulants (200-

THE COMPARATIVE RESULTS OF LONG-TERM ANTICOAGULANT THERAPY FOLLOWING MYOCARDIAL INFARCTION

Author Reference	Manchester 203		Keyes et al. 204		Bjerklund 200		Suzman et al. 205		British Medical Research Council 206		University of Chicago	
Anticoagulant	Dicumarol Sintrom		Dicumarol Hedulin		Dicumarol		Dicumarol Hedulin Cumopyran		Hedulin[++]		Dicumarol Hedulin	
Months of Follow-up	12-120		6-60		1-66		3-76		3-36		24	
	Control	Treated	Control	Treated	Control	Treated	Control	Treated	Control	Treated	Control	Treated
Number of Patients	200	204	234	121	118	119	88	82	188	195	281	201
Causes of Death (Percent)												
Total Cardiovascular	42.5	7.7	44.1	8.2	31.1	20.9	32.8	7.3	16.5	11.2	23.7	9.2
Recurrent Myocardial Infarctions	18.0	2.9	37.4*	5.8*	25.4*	11.8*	21.5	3.7	14.9	9.2	20.2	7.3
Thromboembolic Complications (non-coronary)	8.0	0.9	N.R.[+]	N.R.[+]	1.5@	2.5@	1.1	0	1.6‡	0	1.3	1.1
Congestive Heart Failure	16.5	3.9	6.7	0.8	3.4	3.3	9.1	2.4	0	1.5	2.2	0
Hemorrhage	0	0	0	1.6	0.8	3.3	1.1	1.2	0	0.5	0	0.8
Complications among the Survivors (Percent)												
Total Cardiovascular	45.0	34.4	N.R.[+]	N.R.[+]	N.R.[+]	N.R.[+]	12.5	25.6	50.0	37.1	18.1	14.1
Recurrent Myocardial Infarctions	16.0	11.3	N.R.[+]	5.7	14.4	10.9	5.7	4.9	17.0	3.1	13.4	8.0
Thromboembolic Complications (non-coronary)	9.5	5.9	N.R.[+]	N.R.[+]	N.R.[+]	N.R.[+]	N.R.[+]	N.R.[+]	0	0	4.7	6.1
Congestive Heart Failure	19.5	17.2	N.R.[+]	N.R.[+]	N.R.[+]	N.R.[+]	6.8	20.7	33.0•	34.0•	N.R.[+]	N.R.[+]
Hemorrhage	0	2.9	0	13.2	N.R.[+]	14.4	0	14.6	4.3°	24.6°	0	24.9
Survivors without Complications (Percent)												
	12.5	57.8	54.3†	84.4†	53.4	69.8	54.7	67.1	**	**	58.2	76.4

[++] The control group received a low fixed dose of anticoagulant.
* Includes sudden and unexplained deaths.
[+] N.R., not recorded.
@ Ruptured heart and "arteriosclerotic complications".
‡ Cerebral embolism, 0.5%; other types, 1.1%.
• Male survivors with dyspnea.
° Includes all minor hemorrhages; in the treated group there were 7.6% (15) major hemorrhages.
‡ Includes unspecified number of cardiovascular complications, such as angina pectoris, etc.
** Of 115 male control survivors, 48% had angina; of 126 male survivors who were treated 36% had angina.

206). These five studies and the University of Chicago Study are summarized in Table VII and Figure 6 in which the deaths and complications occurring in each study are tabulated. All reveal a favorable influence in the group treated with anticoagulants. Though there are numerous pitfalls in interpretation of these studies (200, 201), the results are roughly comparable and indicate that patients receiving anticoagulant therapy derive definite benefit during the first two years following myocardial infarction. It will require longer observation before a less qualified conclusion can be made.

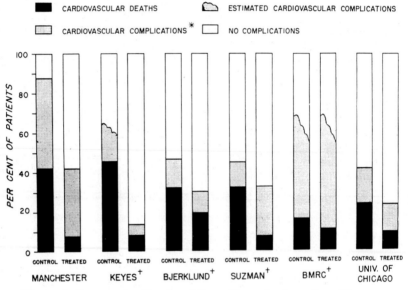

Figure 6. Comparative Results of Long-Term Anticoagulant Therapy.

*Except for the British Medical Research Council Study (BMRC), these figures do not include angina pectoris, but do include non-fatal myocardial infarction, congestive heart failure, and but for the exceptions noted.
+Thromboembolism.

The Laboratory Control of Anticoagulant Therapy. The methods of laboratory control of anticoagulant therapy are not shown in Table VII but as can be seen from the frequency of hemorrhage, none appears ideal. The Proconvertin-Prothrombin test of Owren (207) was used by Bjerklund (202), who found nearly twice the incidence of hemorrhage recorded by Owren. The Quick prothrombin test used in the British and Chicago Studies provides no more consistent control of hemorrhage (4.1 and 24.9%, respectively). Figures regarding the incidence of hemorrhage are not easy to compare because of different criteria used to define hemorrhage, but indicate that a greater risk of hemorrhage is not associated with a reduced mortality rate in the treated group, though there is some hint that it may correlate with a reduced reinfarction rate. This does not mean that inadequate prolongation of the clotting test can be tolerated for in half of the 18 patients of ours, in whom such data were available at the time of reinfarction, the test time was below the prophylactic range.

Conclusion: From these studies, it can be concluded that long-term anticoagulant therapy is distinctly beneficial. However, present techniques are imperfect: they do not prevent all thromboses (201). There still remains a need for a better oral anticoagulant which will consistently prevent thrombosis and not seriously interfere with hemostasis. Whether long-term heparin therapy can approach this ideal, remains to be established. More likely, adequate control of reinfarction will be attained only with more complete understanding of the etiology of thrombosis.

REFERENCES

1. Hunter, W. C., Sneeden, V. D., Robertson, T. D. and Snyder, G. A. C.: Thrombosis of the Deep Veins of the Leg. Arch. Int. Med., *68:* 1, 1941.
2. Ophüls, W.: A Statistical Survey of Three Thousand Autopsies. Stanford University Publications, University Series, Medical Science, *1:* 3, 1921.
3. Hicks, S. P. and Warren, S.: Infarction of the Brain without Thrombosis. Arch. Path., *52:* 403, 1951.
4. Wright, I. S., Marple, C. D. and Beck, D. F.: *Myocardial Infarction.* Grune and Stratton, N. Y., 1954.
5. Levine, S. A. and Brown, C. L.: Coronary Thrombosis: Its Various Clinical Features. Medicine, *8:* 245, 1929.

6. Yater, W. M., Traum, A. H., Brown, W. G., Fitzgerald, R. P., Geisler, M. A. and Wilcox, B. B.: Coronary Artery Disease in Men Eighteen to Thirty-Nine Years of Age. Report of 866 Cases, 450 with Necropsy Examinations, Am. Ht. J., *36:* 334; 683, 1948.

7. Kwaan, H. C., Lo, R. and McFadzean, A. J. S.: On The Lysis of Thrombi Experimentally Produced within Veins. Brit. J. Haemat., *4:* 51, 1958.

8. Wright, H. P.: Characteristics of Blood Platelets. Their Significance in Thrombus Formation, in *Blood Clotting and Allied Problems.* J. E. Flynn, Ed., Trans. of the Fourth Conf., Josiah Macy, Jr. Foundation, 1951, p. 119.

9. Mehrotra, R. M. L.: An Experimental Study of the Changes which Occur in Ligated Arteries and Veins. J. Path. and Bact., *65:* 307, 1953.

10. Poole, J. C. F., Sanders, A. G. and Florey, H. W.: The Regeneration of Aortic Endothelium. J. Path. and Bact., *75:* 133, 1958.

11. Scheinberg, P.: Cerebral Flow in Vascular Disease of the Brain. Am. J. Med., *8:* 139, 1950.

12. Gorlin, R., Brachfield, N., MacLeod, C. and Bopp, P.: Effect of Nitroglycerine on the Coronary Circulation in Patients with Coronary Artery Disease or Increased Left Ventricular Work. Circulation, *19:* 705, 1959.

13. Zoll, P. M., Wessler, S. and Blumgart, H. L.: Angina Pectoris. Am. J. Med., *11:* 331, 1951.

14. Saphir, O., Priest, W. S., Hamburger, W. W. and Katz, L. N.: Coronary Atherosclerosis, Coronary Thrombosis, and the Resulting Myocardial Changes. Am. Ht. J., *10:* 567; 762, 1935.

15. Biggs, R. and Macfarlane, R. G.: *Human Blood Coagulation and Its Disorders,* 2nd. Ed., Charles C. Thomas, Springfield, 1957.

16. Quick, A.: *Hemorrhagic Diseases,* Lea and Febiger, Philadelphia, 1957.

17. Jorpes, J. E.: One Hunderd Years of Research on Blood Coagulation Leading to the Present Day Anticoagulant Therapy in Thrombosis, in *Thrombosis and Embolism. Proc. of the First Internat. Conf.* Benno Schwabe, Basel, 1955, p. 23.

18. Milstone, J. H.: On the Evolution of Blood Clotting Theory. Medicine, *31:* 411, 1952.

19. Macfarlane, R. G.: Blood Coagulation, with Particular Reference to the Early Stages. Physiol. Rev., *36:* 479, 1956.

20. Fisch, U. and Druckert, F.: Some Aspects of Kinetics of the First Stages of Blood Thromboplastin Formation. Thromb. Diath. Haem., *3:* 98, 1959.

21. Biggs, R., Douglas, A. S. and Macfarlane, R. G.: The Formation of Thromboplastin in Human Blood. J. Physiol., *119:* 89, 1953.

22. Bergsagel, D. E. and Houghie, C.: Intermediate Stages in the Formation of Blood Thromboplastin. Brit. J. Haemat., *2:* 113, 1956.

23. Wright, J. H. and Minot, G. R.: The Viscous Metamorphosis of the Blood Platelet. J. Exper. Med., *26:* 395, 1917.

24. Brinkhous, K. M.: Clotting Defect in Hemophilia: Deficiency in a Plasma Factor Required for Platelet Utilization. Proc. Soc. Exp. Biol. and Med., *66:* 117, 1947.

25. Quick, A. J.: Studies on the Enigma of the Hemostatic Dysfunction of Hemophilia. Am. J. Med. Sci., *214:* 272, 1947.

26. Houghie, C.: The Role of Factor V in the Formation of Blood Thromboplastin. J. Lab. Clin. Med., *50:* 61, 1957.

27. Biggs, R., Douglas, A. S. and Macfarlane, R. G.: The Initial Stages of Blood Coagulation. J. Physiol., *122:* 538, 1953.

28. Stefanini, M.: Basic Mechanisms of Hemostasis. Bull. N. Y. Acad. Med., *30:* 239, 1954.

29. Alkjaersig, N., Abe, T. and Seegers, W. H.: Purification and Quantitative Determination of Platelet Factor 3. Am. J. Physiol., *181:* 304, 1955.

30. Rouser, G., White, S. G. and Schloredt, D.: Phospholipid Structure and Thromboplastic Activity. Biochim. Biophys. Acta, *28:* 71, 81, 1958.

31. Troup, S. B. and Reed, C. F.: Platelet Thromboplastic Factor: Its Chemical Nature, In Vitro Activity, and The Identification of Similar Thromboplastic Substances in Red Blood Cells. J. Clin. Invest., *37:* 937, 1958.

32. Bergsagel, D. E.: Viscous Metamorphosis of Platelets. Morphological Platelet Changes by an Intermediate Product of Blood Thromboplastin Formation. Brit. J. Haemat., *2:* 130, 1956.

33. Koller, F.: Le Facteur X. Rev. Hémat., *10:* 362, 1955.

34. Owren, P. A.: The Present State of the Converting and Accelerator Factors in Prothrombin Conversion, in ref. 17, p. 65.

35. Garret, J. V.: The Platelet-Like Activity of Certain Brain Extracts. J. Lab. Clin. Med., *47:* 752, 1956.

36. Chargaff, E.: The Thromboplastic Activity of Tissue Phosphatides. J. Biol. Chem., *155:* 387, 1944.

37. Newlands, M. J. and Wild, F.: Sources of Platelet Factor for the Thromboplastin Generation Test. Nature, London, *176:* 885, 1955.

38. Biggs, R. and Bidwell, E.: An Attempt to Identify a Single Phospholipid Active in Blood Coagulation. Brit. J. Haemat., *3:* 387, 1957.

39. Robinson, D. S. and Poole, J. C. F.: The Similar Effect of Chylomicra and Ethanolamine Phosphatide on the Generation of Thrombin During Coagulation. Quart. J. Exp. Physiol., *41:* 36, 1956.

40. Chargaff, E.: Studies on the Mechanism of the Thromboplastic Effect. J. Biol. Chem., *173:* 253, 1948.

41. Hecht, E. R., Cho, M. H. and Seegers, W. H.: Thromboplastin: Nomenclature and Preparation of Protein-Free Material Different from Platelet Factor 3 or Lipid Activator. Am. J. Physiol., *193:* 584, 1958.

42. Wallach, D. F. H., Maurice, P. A., Steele, B. B. and Surgenour, D. M.: Studies on the Relationship between the Colloidal State and Clot Promoting Activity of Pure Phosphatidylethanalamine. J. Biol. Chem., *234:* 2829, 1959.

43. Boyle, P. W.: Particle Size as a Factor in Thromboplastin Formation. Blood, *14:* 1063, 1959.

44. Marcus, A. J. and Spaet, T. H.: Platelet Phosphatides: Their Separation, Identification and Clotting Activity. J. Clin. Invest., *37:* 1836, 1958.

45. Barkhan, P., Silver, M. J., DaCosta, P. B. and Tocantins, L. M.: Phosphatidylserine and Blood Coagulation. Nature, *182:* 1031, 1958.

46. Silver, M. J., Turner, D. L. and Tocantins, L. M.: Lipid Anticoagulants, in Prog. in Hemat. II, L. M. Tocantins, Ed., Grune and Stratton, N. Y., 1959, p. 264.

47. Seegers, W. H.: Coagulation of the Blood. Adv. in Enzym., *16:* 23, 1955.

48. Seegers, W. H., Loomis, E. C. and Vandenbelt, J. M.: Electrophoresis of Purified Prothrombin. Proc. Soc. Exp. Biol. and Med., *56:* 70, 1944.

49. Miller, K. D. and Seegers, W. H.: The Preparation of a Carbohydrate Fraction from Prothrombin and Its Chemical Nature. Arch. Biochem. and Biophys., *60:* 398, 1956.

50. Schultz, H. E. and Schwick, G.: Über den Mechanismus der

Thrombinbildung im Isolierten System. Z. Physiol. Chem., *289:* 26, 1951.

51. Laki, L.: Chemistry of Prothrombin and Some of Its Reactions. Physiol. Rev., *34:* 730, 1954.
52. Scheraga, H. A. and Laskowski, M., Jr.: The Fibrinogen-Fibrin Conversion. Adv. in Protein Chem., XII: 1, 1957.
53. Laki, K., Kominz, D. R., Symonds, P., Lorand, L. and Seegers, W. H.: The Amino Acid Composition of Bovine Prothrombin. Arch. Biochem., *49:* 276, 1954.
54. Warner, E. D. and Carter, J. R.: Importance of Disulfide in Blood Clotting, in ref. 17, p. 61.
55. Laki, K.: The Clotting of Fibrinogen. Blood, *8:* 845, 1953.
56. Ferry, J. D.: Protein Gels. Adv. in Prot. Chem., *IV:* 1, 1948.
57. Guest, M. M. and Ware, A. G.: Fibrinolytic Activity of Purified Thrombin. Science, *112:* 21, 1950.
58. Lorand, L. and Middlebrook, W. R.: The Action of Thrombin on Fibrinogen. Biochem. J., *52:* 196, 1952.
59. Sherry, S., Troll, W. and Glueck, H.: Thrombin as a Proteolytic Enzyme. Physiol. Rev., *34:* 736, 1954.
60. Lorand, L.: Fibrino-peptide. Biochem. J., *52:* 200, 1952.
61. Sherry, S. and Troll, W.: The Action of Thrombin on Synthetic Substrates. J. Biol. Chem., *208:* 95, 1954.
62. Lorand, L. and Middlebrook, W. R.: Species Specificity of Fibrinogen as Revealed by End-Group Studies. Science, *118:* 515, 1953.
63. Sizer, I. W.: The Inhibition of Blood Clotting *in Vitro* and *in Vivo* by Tyrosinase. Science, *116:* 275, 1952.
64. Lorand, L.: Interaction of Thrombin and Fibrinogen. Physiol. Rev., *34:* 742, 1954.
65. Bailey, K. and Bettleheim, F. R.: The Nature of the Fibrinogen-Thrombin Reaction. Brit. Med. Bull., *11:* 50, 1955.
66. Laki, K. and Lorand, L.: On the Solubility of Fibrin Clots. Science, *108:* 280, 1948.
67. Lorand, L., Jacobsen, A. and Fuchs, L. E.: In *Symposium on Sulfur in Proteins*. R. Benesch et al., Eds., Acad. Press, N. Y., 1959, p. 109.
68. Jensen, E. V.: Sulfhydryl-Disulfide Interchange. Science, *130:* 1319, 1959.
69. Hawn, C. V. Z. and Porter, K. R.: The Fine Structure of Clots Formed From Purified Bovine Fibrinogen and Thrombin: A

Study with the Electron Microscope. J. Exper. Med., *86:* 285, 1947.

70. Chargaff, E.: The Coagulation of Blood. Adv. in Enzymol., *5:* 31, 1945.

71. Poole, J. C. F.: Fats and Blood Coagulation. Brit. Med. Bull., *14:* 253, 1958.

72. Marinetti, G. V., Erbland, J. and Kochen, J.: Quantitative Chromatography of Phsophatides. Fed. Proc., *16:* 837, 1957.

73. Poole, J. C. F., Robinson, D. S. and Macfarlane, R. G.: The Action of Russel's Viper Venom and Lecithin on the Coagulation of Plasma. Quart. J. Exp. Physiol., *40:* 276, 1955.

74. Poole, J. C. F. and Robinson, D. S.: A Comparison of the Effects of Certain Phosphatides and of Chylomicra on Plasma Coagulation in the Presence of Russel's Viper Venom. Quart. J. Exp. Physiol., *41:* 31, 1956.

75. Poole, J. C. F. and Robinson, D. S.: Further Observations on Effects of Ethanolamine Phosphatide on Plasma Coagulation. Quart. J. Exp. Physiol., *41:* 295, 1956.

76. O'Brien, J. R.: The Similarity of the Action of Phosphatidylethanolamine and Platelets in Blood Coagulation. J. Clin. Path., *9:* 47, 1956.

77. Cohen, L.: Serum Phospholipids in Coronary Artery Disease. J. Lab. Clin. Med., *54:* 352, 1959.

78. Poole, J. C. F.: The Effect of Certain Fatty Acids on the Coagulation of Plasma *in Vitro.* Brit. J. Exp. Path., *36:* 248, 1955.

79. Pilkington, T. R. E.: The Effect of Fatty Acids and Detergents on the Calcium Clotting Time of Human Plasma. Clin. Sci., *16:* 269, 1957.

80. O'Brien, J. R.: The Effect of Some Fatty Acids and Phospholipids on Blood Coagulation. Brit. J. Exp. Path., *38:* 529, 1957.

81. Fullerton, H. W., Davie, W. J. A. and Anastosopoulos, G.: Relationship of Alimentary Lipemia to Blood Coagulability. Brit. Med. J., *2:* 250, 1953.

82. O'Brien, J. R.: Some Postprandial Effects of Eating Various Phospholipids and Triglycerides. Lancet, *1:*1213, 1957.

83. O'Brien, J. R.: Relation of Blood-Coagulation to Lipaemia. Lancet, *2:* 690, 1955.

84. Mersky, C. and Nossel, H. L.: Blood Coagulation After the Ingestion of Saturated and Unsaturated Fats. Lancet, *1:* 806, 1957.

85. Tulloch, J. A., Overman, R. S. and Wright, I. S.: Failure of In-

gestion of Cream to Affect Blood Coagulation. Am. J. Med., *14:* 674, 1953.

86. O'Brien, J. R.: Effect of a Meal of Eggs and Different Fats on Blood Coagulability. Lancet, *2:* 232, 1956.

87. Dole, V. P.: A Relation Between Non-Esterified Fatty Acids in Plasma and the Metabolism of Glucose. J. Clin. Invest., *35:* 150, 1956.

88. Fredrickson, D. S. and Gordon, R. S., Jr.: Transport of Fatty Acids. Physiol. Rev., *38:* 585, 1958.

89. Tilden, J. H. and Shipley, R. E.: Effect of Glucose on Appearance of Plasma-Clotting Accelerator Activity, Lactescene, and Plasma Lipids in Fat-Fed Dogs, Circ. Res., *6:* 804, 1958.

90. Waldron, J. M., Beidelman, B. and Duncan, G. F.: Inhibition of the Clot-Accelerating Property of Ingested Fat by Simultaneous Feeding of Sugar. J. Appl. Physiol., *4:* 761, 1952.

91. Thomas, W. A. and Hartroft, W. S.: Myocardial Infarction in Rats Fed Diets Containing High Fat Cholesterol, Thiouracil and Sodium Cholate. Circulation, *19:* 65, 1959.

92. Brinkhous, K. M.: Blood Clotting: The Plasma Procoagulants. Ann. Rev. Physiol., *21:* 271, 1959.

93. Storm, O. and Hansen, A. T.: Mitral Commisurotomy Performed During Anticoagulant Prophylaxis with Dicumarol. Circulation, *12:* 981, 1955.

94. Magnus, G.: Über den Vorgang der Blutstillung. Arch. f. Klin. Chir., *125:* 612, 1923.

95. Zucker, M. B.: Platelet Agglutination and Vasoconstriction as Factors in Spontaneous Hemostasis in Normal, Thrombocytopenic, Heparinized and Hypoprothrombinemic Rats. Am. J. Physiol., *148:* 275, 1947.

96. Ackeroyd, J. F.: Role of Platelets in Coagulation, Thrombosis and Haemostasis, with Some Observations on Platelet Dysfunction Including Thrombosthenia. Brit. Med. Bull., *11:* 21, 1955.

97. Lutz, B.: Intravascular Agglutination of the Formed Elements of Blood. Physiol. Rev., *31:* 107, 1951.

98. Zucker, M. J.: Serotonin (5-hydroxytryptamine): Hematologic Aspects. p. 206 in ref. 46.

99. Ware, A. G., Fahey, J. L. and Seegers, W. H.: Platelet Extracts. Fibrin Formation and Interaction of Purified Prothrombin and Thromboplastin. Am. J. Physiol., *154:* 140, 1948.

100. Van Creveld, S. and Paulssen, M. M. P.: Isolation and Properties

of the Third Clotting Factor in Blood-Platelets. Lancet, *1:* 23, 1952.

101. Tocantins, L. M.: Platelets and the Spontaneous Syneresis of Blood Clots. Am. J. Physiol., *110:* 278, 1934.

102. Ballerini, G. and Seegers, W. H.: A Description of Clot Retraction as a Visual Experience. Thromb. Diasth. Haem., *3:* 147, 1959.

103. Quick, A. J. and Favre-Gilly, J. E.: Fibrin, a Factor Influencing the Consumption of Prothrombin in Coagulation. Am. J. Physiol., *158:* 387, 1949.

104. Link, K. P.: The Anticoagulant from Spoiled Sweet Clover Hay. The Harvey Lectures, *39:* 162, 1944.

105. Link, K. P.: The Discovery of Dicumarol and its Sequels. Circulation, *19:* 97, 1959.

106. Kabat, H., Stohlman, E. F. and Smith, M. I.: Hypoprothrombinemia Induced by Administration of Indanedione Derivatives. J. Pharmacol. and Exp. Therap., *80:* 160, 1944.

107. Hunter, R. B. and Sheperd, D. M.: Chemistry of Coumarin Anticoagulant Drugs. Brit. Med. Bull., *11:* 56, 1955.

108. Stahmann, M. A., Wolff, I. A. and Link, K. P.: Hydroxycoumarins. I. Synthesis of 4-hydroxy-coumarins. J. Am. Chem. Soc., *65:* 2285, 1943.

109. Mentzer, C.: Les Divers Groupes de Substances Synthétiques Douées d'une Activité Antivitaminique K, et la Signification Biologique des Résultats Obtenus. Bull. Soc. Chim. Biol. Paris, *30:* 872, 1948.

110. Naeye, R. L.: Hemophilioid Factors: Acquired Deficiencies in Several Hemorrhagic States. Proc. Soc. Exp. Biol. and Med., *94:* 623, 1957.

111. Martius, C. and Nitz-Litzow, D.: Über den Wirkungs-Mechanismus des Dicoumarol und Verwandter Verbindungen. Bioch. and Biophys. Acta, *13:* 152, 289, 1954.

112. Friedkin, M. and Lehninger, A. L.: Esterification of Inorganic Phosphate Coupled to Electron Transport Between Dihydro-diphosphopyridine Nucleotide and Oxygen. J. Biol. Chem., *178:* 611, 1949.

113. Beyer, R. E.: Vitamin K_1, a Component of the Mitochondrial Oxidative Phosphorylation System. Biochim. and Biophysica Acta, *28:* 663, 1958.

114. Cooper, C. and Lehninger, A. L.: Oxidative Phosphorylation by an Enzyme Complex from Extracts of Mitochondria. J. Biol. Chem., *219:* 519, 1956.

115. Chance, B. and Williams, G. R.: The Respiratory Chain and Oxidative Phosphorylation. Adv. in Enzymol., *17:* 65, 1956.

116. Lee, C. C., Trevoy, L. W., Spinks, J. W. T. and Jacques, L. B.: Dicoumarol Labelled with C^{14}. Proc. Soc. Exp. Biol. and Med., *74:* 151, 1950.

117. Lupton, A. M.: The Effect of Perfusion Through the Isolated Liver on the Prothrombin of Blood from Normal and Dicoumarol Treated Rats. J. Pharmacol. and Exp. Therap., *89:* 306, 1947.

118. Brown, W. D.: Reversible Effects of Anticoagulants and Protamine on Alimentary Lipemia. Quart. J. Exp. Physiol., *37:* 75, 1952.

119. Burns, J. J., Weiner, M., Simon, G. and Brodie, B. B.: The Biotransformation of Ethylbiscoumacetate (Tromexan®) in Man, Rabbit and Dog. J. Pharmacol., *108:* 33, 1953.

120. Schulert, A. R. and Weiner, M.: The Physiological Disposition of Phenylindanedione in Man. J. Pharmacol., *110:* 451, 1954.

121. Jaques, L. B.: The Physiology of the Anticoagulants. Rev. d'Hemat., *10:* 379, 1955.

122. Pollock, B. E.: Clinical Experience with Warfarin (Coumadin®) Sodium, A New Anticoagulant. J. A. M. A., *159:* 1094, 1955.

123. Weiner, M., Brodie, B. B., and Burns, J. J.: A Comparative Study of Hypoprothrombinemic Agents: The Physiologic Disposition and Chemical Pharmacology of Coumarin and Indanedione Compounds. p. 181 in ref. 17.

124. Sougin-Mibashan, R. and Horowitz, M.: The Uricosuric Action of Ethylbiscoumacetate. Lancet, *1:* 1191, 1955.

125. Pastorova, V. E. and Kudryashav, B. A.: Strength of Capillaries in Antagonistic Interaction of Dicoumarin and Vitamin K in Animal Organisms. Doklady Acad. Nauk. S.S.S.R., *107:* 340–2, 1956, in Chem. Abst., *50:* 10919, 1956.

126. Jordal, R.: Necrosing Cutaneous Hemorrhages as a Complication in Dicoumarol Treatment. Acta Med. Scandinav., *154:* 477, 1956.

127. Fischer, R., Bircher, J. and Reich, T.: Der Haarausfall nach Antikoagulierender Therapie. Schweiz. Med. Wchnschr., *83:* 509, 1953.

128. Pastor, B. H. and Tetreault, A. F.: Agranulocytosis and Scarlatiniform Eruption due to Phenindione. J. A. M. A., *161:* 873, 1956.

129. McLean, J.: The Discovery of Heparin. Circulation, *19:* 75, 1959.

130. Howell, W. H. and Holt, E.: Two New Factors in Blood Coagulation—Heparin and Antithrombin. Am. J. Physiol., *47:* 238, 1918.

131. Charles, A. F. and Scott, D. A.: Studies on Heparin. II. Heparin in Various Tissues. J. Biol. Chem., *102:* 431, 1933.

132. Charles, A. F. and Scott, D. A.: Studies on Heparin. IV. Observations on the Chemistry of Heparin. Biochem. J., *30:* 1927, 1936.

133. Craaford, C.: Preliminary Report on Postoperative Treatment with Heparin as Preventative of Thrombosis. Acta Chir. Scandinav., *79:* 407, 1937.

134. Best, C. H.: Preparation of Heparin and Its Use in the First Clinical Cases. Circulation, *19:* 79, 1959.

135. Jaques, L. B., Bell, H. J. and Cho, M. H.: The Physiology of Heparin. p. 281, in ref. 17.

136. Walton, K. W.: Chemistry and Mode of Action of Heparin and Related Compounds. Brit. Med. Bull., *11:* 62, 1955.

137. Wolfrom, M. L. and Rice, F. A. H.: Uronic Acid Component of Heparin. J. Am. Chem. Soc., *68:* 532, 1946.

138. Jorpes, J. E. and Bergstrom, S.: Heparin: A Mucoitin-polysulfuric Acid. J. Biol. Chem., *118:* 447, 1937.

139. Charles, A. F. and Todd, A. R.: Observations on the Structure of the Barium Salt of Heparin. Biochem. J., *34:* 112, 1940.

140. Wolfrom, M. L., Montgomery, R., Korabinus, J. V. and Rathgeb, P.: The Structure of Heparin. J. Am. Chem. Soc., *75:* 5796, 1953.

141. Wilander, O.: Studies on Heparin, Skandinav. Arch. f. Physiol. Suppl. *15:* 1, 1938.

142. Jorpes, J. E., Boström, H. and Mutt, V.: The Linkage of the Amino Group in Heparin. J. Biol. Chem., *183:* 607, 1950.

143. Smellman, O., Sylvén, B. and Julén, C.: Analysis of the Native-Heparin-Lipoprotein Complex Including the Identification of Heparin Complement (Heparin Co-factor) Obtained from Extracts of Tissue Mast Cells. Biochem. et Biophys. Acta, *7:* 98, 1951.

144. Foster, A. B. and Huggard, A. J.: The Chemistry of Heparin. Adv. in Carbohyd. Chem., *10:* 335, 1955.

145. Ferguson, J. H. and Glazko, A. J.: Heparin. J. Lab. Clin. Med., *26:* 1559, 1941.

146. Klein, P. D. and Seegers, W. H.: The Nature of Plasma Antithrombin Activity. Blood, *5:* 742, 1950.

147. Douglas, A. S.: Antihemophilic Globulin Consumption During Blood Coagulation. Blood, *11:* 423, 1956.
148. Solandt, P. Y. and Best, C. H.: Heparin and Coronary Thrombosis in Experimental Animals. Lancet, *2:* 130, 1938.
149. Hoch, H. and Chanutin, A.: Effects of Anticoagulants on Serum and Plasma. J. Biol. Chem., *197:* 503, 1952.
150. Chargaff, E., Ziff, M. and Cohen, S. S.: The Reaction Between Heparin and the Thromboplastic Factor. J. Biol. Chem., *136:* 257, 1940.
151. Overman, R. S.: The Chemical Purification and Mode of Action of a Thromboplastic Inhibitor, in *Blood Clotting and Allied Problems.* Ed. J. E. Flynn, Trans. of the Second Conf., Jos. Macy, Jr. Found., N. Y. 1949, p. 29.
152. Jaques, L. B.: Heparinase. J. Biol. Chem., *133:* 445, 1940.
153. Weiss, W. A., Gilman, J. S., Catenacci, A. J. and Ostenberg, A. E.: Heparin Neutralization with Polybrene Administered Intravenously. J. A. M. A., *166:* 603, 1958.
154. Sorenson, C. W. and Wright, I. S.: A Synthetic Anticoagulant: A Polysulfuric Acid Ester of Polyanhydromannuronic Acid (Paritol). Circulation, *2:* 658, 1950.
155. Hirschboeck, J. S. and Madison, F. W.: A Comparison of the Anticoagulant Properties of a Polyhexuronic Acid Ester with Sodium Heparin. J. Lab. Clin. Med., *36:* 836, 1950.
156. Halse, T.: Fortschritte bei der Behandlung der Akuten Thrombose, Thrombophlebitis und Embolie mit Heparin, Dicumarol und Thrombocid. Dtsch. med. Wschr., *74:* 1326, 1949.
157. Ricketts, C. R., Walton, K. W., Van Leuven, B. D., Birbeck, A., Brown, A., Kennedy, A. C. and Burt, C. C.: Therapeutic Trial of the Synthetic Heparin Analogue Dextran Sulfate. Lancet, *2:* 1004, 1953.
158. Studer, A., Engelberg, R. and Randall, L. O.: Zur Frage der Toxizität von Heparinoiden. p. 863–868 in ref. 17.
159. McDevitt, E., Huebner, R. D. and Wright, I. S.: Ineffectiveness of Heparin by Sublingual Administration. J. A. M. A., *148:* 1123, 1952.
160. Haach, E. W.: Hypersensitivity to Heparin: Report of 3 Cases. Proc. Mayo Clinic, *27:* 163, 1952.
161. Sherry, S., Fletcher, A. P. and Alkjaersig, N.: Fibrinolysis and Fibrinolytic Activity in Man. Physiol. Rev., *39:* 343, 1959.
162. Biggs, R., Macfarlane, R. G. and Pilling, J.: Observations on

Fibrinolysis. Experimental Activity Produced by Exercise or Adrenaline. Lancet, *1:* 402, 1947.

163. Kruse, I. and Dam, H.: The Inactivation of Thromboplastin by Cobra Venom. Biochim. et Biophys. Acta, *5:* 268, 1950.

164. Shulman, S., Alkjaersig, N. and Sherry S.: Physicochemical Studies on Human Plasminogen (Profibrinolysin) and Plasmin (Fibrinolysin). J. Biol. Chem., *233:* 9, 1958.

165. Blomback, B. and Blomback, M.: Purification of Human and Bovine Fibrinoven. Arkiv. Kem., *10:* 415, 1956, cited in ref. 161.

166. Lassen, M.: Heat Denaturation of Plasminogen in the Fibrin Plate Method. Acta Physiol. Scandinav., *27:* 371, 1952.

167. Alkjaersig, N., Fletcher, A. P. and Sherry, S.: Activation of Human Plasminogen I. Spontaneous Activation in Glycerol. J. Biol. Chem., *233:* 81, 1958.

168. Kwaan, H. C., Lo, R. and McFadzean, A. J. S.: Inhibition of Plasma Fibrinolytic Activity by Exercised Ischemic Muscles. Clin. Sci., *17:* 361, 1958.

169. Astrup, T. and Permin, P. M.: Fibrinolysis in the Animal Organism. Nature, *159:* 681, 1947.

170. Astrup, T. and Sterndorff, I.: Fibrinolysokinase Activity in Animal and Human Tissue. Acta Physiol. Scandinav., *37:* 40, 1956.

171. Barnett, E. V. and Baron, S.: Cell Culture Produced Activator for Serum Proteolytic Proenzyme and its Presence in Poliomyelitis Vaccine. Fed. Proc., *17:* 503, 1958.

172. Mullertz, S.: Activation of Plasminogen. Ann. N. Y. Acad. Sci., *68:* 38, 1957.

173. Mullertz, S.: A Plasminogen Activator in Spontaneously Active Human Blood. Proc. Soc. Exp. Biol. and Med., *82:* 291, 1953.

174. Albrechtsen, O. K., Storm, O., and Trolle, D.: Fibrinolytic Activity in the Circulating Blood Following Amniotic Fluid Infusion. Acta Haemat., *14:* 309, 1955.

175. Albrechtsen, O. K. and Thaysen, J. H.: Fibrinolytic Activity in Human Saliva. Acta Physiol. Scandinav., *35:* 138, 1955.

176. Storm, O.: Fibrinolytic Activity in Human Tears. Scand. J. Clin. and Lab. Invest., *7:* 55, 1955.

177. Astrup, T. and Sterndorff, I.: A Fibrinolytic System in Human Milk. Proc. Soc. Exp. Biol. Med., *84:* 605, 1953.

178. Lundquist, F., Thorsteinsson, Th. Buus, O.: Purification and Properties of Some Enzymes in Human Seminal Plasma. Biochem. J., *59:* 69, 1955.

179. Sherry, S. and Alkjaersig, N.: Fibrinolytic Enzyme of Human Plasma. Thromb. et Diath. Haem., *1:* 264, 1957.
180. Ploug, J., Kjeldgaard, N. O.: Urokinase, and Activator of Plasminogen from Human Urine. I. Isolation and Properties. Biochim. et Biophys. Acta, *24:* 278, 1957.
181. von Kualla, K. N.: Intravenous Protein—Free Pyrogen, A Powerful Fibrinolytic Agent in Man. Circulation, *17:* 187, 1958.
182. Fletcher, A. P. and Johnson, A. J.: Methods Employed for the Purification of Streptokinase. Proc. Soc. Exp. Biol. and Med., *94:* 233, 1957.
183. Sherry, S.: Fibrinolytic Activity of Streptokinase Activated Human Plasmin. J. Clin. Invest., *33:* 1054, 1954.
184. Jacobssen, K.: Studies on Trypsin and Plasmin Inhibitors in Human Blood Serum. Scand. J. Clin. Lab. Invest., *7:* Suppl. 14, 1955.
185. Shulman, N. R.: Physiological Aspects of Variations in Proteolytic Inhibition. J. Exp. Med., *95:* 605, 1952.
186. Astrup, T.: Role of Blood Coagulation and Fibrinolysis in the Pathogenesis of Arteriosclerosis, in *Connective Tissue, Thrombosis and Atherosclerosis.* I. H. Page, ed., Academic Press, N. Y., 1959, p. 223.
187. *Fibrinolysin Precursors and Inhibitors in the Coagulation of Blood: Methods of Study.* L. M. Tocantins, ed., Grune and Stratton, N. Y., 1955. Chapter X, p. 161.
188. Grieg, H. B. W. and Runde, I. A.: Studies on the Inhibition of Fibrinolysis by Lipids. Lancet, *2:* 461, 1957.
189. Kwaan, H. C. and McFadzean, A. J. S.: Inhibition of Fibrinolysis *in vivo* by Feeding Cholesterol. Nature, *179:* 260, 1957.
190. McDonald, G. A. and Fullerton, H. W.: Effect of Physical Activity on Increased Coagulability of Blood after Ingestion of High-Fat Meal. Lancet, *2:* 600, 1958.
191. O'Neal, R. M., Thomas, W. A. and Tillman, R. W.: Butter, Corn Oil and Fibrinolysis in Rats. Proc. 32nd. Ann. Meeting of the Central Soc. Clin. Res., Abs. 105, J. Lab. Clin. Med., *54:* 932, 1959.
192. Fletcher, A. P., Alkjaersig, N., Smyrniotis, F. E. and Sherry, S.: The Treatment of Patients Suffering from Early Myocardial Infarction with Massive and Prolonged Streptokinase Therapy. Trans. Ass. Am. Phys., *71:* 287, 1958.
193. Moser, K. M.: Effect of Intravenous Administration of Fibrinolysin (Plasmin) in Man. Circulation, *20:* 42, 1959.

194. Clifton, E. E.: The Use of Plasmin in Humans. Ann. N. Y. Acad. Sci., *68:* 209, 1957.
195. Wright, H. P., Kubik, M. M. and Hayden, M.: Influence of Anticoagulant Administration on the Rate of Recanalization of Experimentally Thrombosed Veins. Brit. J. Surg., *40:* 163, 1952-3.
196. Wright, H. P. and Kubik, M. M.: Recanalization of Thrombosed Arteries under Anticoagulant Therapy. Brit. Med. J., *1:* 1021, 1953.
197. Zollinger, H. U. and Papacharalampous, N.: Über das Appositionelle Proximale Wachstunder Coronarthromben. Schweiz. Med. Wschr., *83:* 864, 1953.
198. Russek, H. I. and Zohman, B. L.: Selection of Patients for Anticoagulant Therapy in Acute Myocardial Infarction. Am. J. M. Sc., *228:* 133, 1954.
199. Gilchrist, A. R. and Tulloch, J. A.: An Evaluation of Anticoagulant Therapy in Acute Myocardial Infarction. Scott. Med. J., *1:* 1, 1956.
200. Bjerklund, C. J.: The Effects of Long-Term Treatment with Dicumarol in Myocardial Infarction. Acta Med. Scand. Suppl. 330, 1957.
201. Bay, E. B., Adams, W. R., Jones, R. J., Page, R. G. and Seide, M.: The Use of Anticoagulant Drugs in Ambulatory Patients. Circulation, *9:* 741, 1954.
202. Tanzi, F. and Van Ness, A. L.: Long-Term Anticoagulant Therapy of the Ambulatory Patient Following Myocardial Infarction. Med. Clin. N. Am., 25, Jan. 1957.
203. Manchester, B.: The Value of Continuous (1 to 10 years) Long-Term Anticoagulant Therapy. Ann. Int. Med., *47:* 1202, 1957.
204. Keyes, J. W., Drake, E. H., James, T. N. and Smith, F. J.: Survival Rates After Myocardial Infarctions with and without Long-Term Anticoagulant Therapy. Am. J. Med. Sci., *226:* 607, 1953.
205. Suzman, M. M., Ruskin, H. D. and Goldberg, B.: An Evaluation of the Effect of Continuous Long-Term Anticoagulant Therapy on the Prognosis of Myocardial Infarction. Circulation, *12:* 338, 1955.
206. Brit. Med. Res. Council: An Assessment of Long-Term Anticoagulant Administration after Cardiac Infarction. Brit. Med. J., *5125:* 803, 1959.
207. Owren, P. A.: Long-Term Dicumarol Treatment in Cardiovascular Disease, in ref. 17, p. 1085.

208. Nomenclature of Blood Clotting Factors. Thromb. Diasth. Haem., *3:* 435, 1959.

209. Wright, I. S.: Concerning the Functions and Nomenclature of Blood Clotting Factors, with a Preliminary Report of the Profile of Blood Clotting Factors in Young Males. Ann. Int. Med., *51:* 841, 1959.

SECTION III
ATHEROSCLEROSIS

Chapter I

THE ATHEROSCLEROTIC PLAQUE

The Arterioscleroses. Arteriosclerosis, or hardening of the arteries, is a general term applied to those pathologic processes, originally considered to be degenerative, which lead to thickening, loss of elasticity and stiffening of the arterial wall. With the accumulation of later knowledge of the histopathology, three major types of arteriosclerosis are now distinguished in most pathology textbooks (1) :

    1. Arteriolosclerosis
    2. Medial Sclerosis of Mönckeberg
    3. Atherosclerosis

Arteriolosclerosis is a hyperplasia of the intima and media of the arterioles throughout the body; it is seen in conjunction with high blood pressure of any cause. *Medial sclerosis* is a hyalinization leading to ultimate calcification and even focal bone formation in the media of larger arteries, particularly those supplying the large muscle groups of the extremities. *Atherosclerosis* is the tissue reaction to the focal deposition of lipid just beneath the intima of the aorta and its main branches to the heart, brain and viscera, and, in consequence, is the most common and most important basis for morbidity and mortality due to arteriosclerosis.

In experimental atherosclerosis, the initial deposit of fatty material is at first extracellular but is later seen in phagocytes, called lipophages. If the accumulation of lipid material exceeds its removal by the venous and lymphatic drainage or local metabolism of the arterial wall, a visible plaque develops and at this time, sometimes earlier, local fibrosis plus fragmentation of the internal elastic lamina may be seen microscopically. As the plaque enlarges, the central portion may become of porridge-like consistency (Gr. *Athero*), surrounded by hyalinized fibrous tissue. Ultimately calcification and even bone formation may take place in this lesion.

While the degenerative changes of hyalinization, calcification

101

and bone formation are the same in Mönckeberg's medial sclerosis and atherosclerosis, the two are considered to be independent processes taking place in different portions of the arterial wall, and largely in different types of arteries (2). Frequently the intimal lesions are seen without medial sclerosis, and *vice versa,* yet they often occur together. Furthermore, while arteriolosclerosis is certainly distinct from atherosclerosis, the latter is certainly intensified, if not frequently precipitated, by the presence of a high blood pressure. It should be noted there are other arterial intimal lesions which are apparently distinct from atherosclerosis in that they present little or no lipid incorporation and show instead predominant muscular or fibrous thickening, with or without myxomatous degeneration. All types of arteriosclerosis are seen more frequently but not necessarily with advancing age.

Complications. The consequences of arterial deterioration are negligible as long as the artery neither leaks nor retards flow. Rupture of some arteries may occur at the site of congenital, mycotic or arteriosclerotic aneurysms; aortic rupture can also occur from a rare type of medial degeneration, cystic medial necrosis (3). An experimental curiosity is the observation that aortic aneurysm and rupture can be induced in the rat by sweet pea poisoning (Lathyrism); the responsible agent appears to be an enzyme poison, identified as a nitrile (4).

By far the most common consequence of arterial disease is occlusion, which is of greatest import when it occurs in arteries supplying vital organs such as the heart and brain. These arteries are most often occluded by atherosclerosis or its complications in which case we note clinical disease, if the involved tissue is not adequately supplied by collateral circulation. For example, coronary artery occlusion is secondary to atherosclerosis in at least 95% of cases (1). Coronary occlusive disease can often be recognized before death, with aid of the electrocardiogram and by virtue of the rather consistent clinical picture it may produce, in contrast to involvement of some other arterial beds. This fact, as well as the great frequency of coronary artery disease, has made it the subject for intensive study recently, while most of the older chemical studies and many animal experiments deal exclusively with aortic atheromata.

In the following discussions, it will be necessary to keep in mind the reservation that all of the factors involved in coronary atherogenesis may not be equally important in the pathogenesis of the aortic disease.

ROLE OF THE ATHEROMATOUS PLAQUE IN CORONARY OCCLUSION

In the detailed autopsy studies of the coronary branches by Blumgart, Schlesinger, and Davis (5), it was found that symptoms of coronary disease occurred only after one or more coronary occlusions. Infarction of the myocardium occurred either after sudden occlusion which was, with rare exception, based upon atherosclerosis or after prolonged myocardial anoxia related to old narrowing or occlusions in the coronary arteries (1, 2). Thus it would seem that ischemic myocardial disease might be all but eradicated, if atherosclerosis could be avoided. However, in a recent exhaustive post-mortem study of the degree and extent of atherosclerosis (6), people dying of unrelated diseases were found to present about two-thirds as much atherosclerosis as those dying of coronary "catastrophes." Let us consider further, then, exactly how this process leads to coronary occlusion.

In a large series of cases of fatal coronary disease in young American soldiers, 90% had either sclerotic or thrombotic occlusion, or both, in about equal frequency; only 10% had no frank occlusion of any artery (7). Wartman, on the other hand, estimated from his series that 60% of coronary occlusions were precipitated by hemorrhage into the intimal plaque (8). There is as yet no agreement as to what mechanism is predominant, but each of the mechanisms depicted in Figure 1 may make some contribution to the overall total of coronary occlusions and myocardial infarctions (listed roughly in order of their frequency):

Thrombosis (1, Figure 1) occurs when the plaque slows the blood flow or provides thrombogenic substances; the possible importance of other coagulation factors has been discussed (page 42). *Progressive narrowing* of the lumen by growth of the plaque until occlusion occurs is conceivable, but this is frequently gradual enough that collateral circulation can develop to perhaps minimize the area of myocardial infarction (9). *Hemorrhage* into the soft core of a plaque may narrow (2, Figure 1) or even occlude (3, Figure 1) the arterial lumen by hematoma formation. *Rupture of an expanding hematoma* into the lumen, may leave a ragged ulcerated base which might predispose to thrombosis (4, Figure 1); *an intimal ulcer* may also result from rupture of a softened atheroma from some cause other than hemorrhage (5, Figure 1). *Embolization* may also result from rupture of a softened atheroma, the porridge-like material occluding the more distal ramifications, or forming a nidus for thrombosis in small branches which might propagate back into arteries of larger caliber (6, Figure 1). The above discussion is necessary to appreciate the importance of two fundamental determinants of manifest coronary disease: a large lumen-compromising plaque and thrombosis; the actual significance of hemorrhage remains to be defined.

In a myriad of animal experiments it has been possible to induce plaque formation by various manipulations of diet, hormones, etc., which occasion a rise in serum lipids. The extent of plaque formation, at least in the great vessels, usually correlates directly with the height of the serum lipid. Other factors being equal, the size of the lumen-encroaching plaque is determined by the elevation of the serum lipids and its duration.

While a connection between serum lipids and plaque formation has been well established, both in animal experiments and in clinical and epidemiological studies, coronary occlusion has not usually been seen in animals. Recently thromboses have been induced in rats but only by drastic dietary and hormonal manipulations (10). As noted above, thrombosis is perhaps more fundamental to the morbidity and mortality in man than plaque formation and, inasmuch as both are apparently influenced by serum lipids (see pages 52, 74 & 121), may this not explain their frequent concurrence? Let us keep atherosclerosis and thrombosis separate in our thinking as we review the current theories of atheroma formation.

THEORIES OF ATHEROMA FORMATION

The Lipid Infiltration Theory. This has changed little since the day of Virchow, and was outlined on page 101. As it is viewed today (1, 2, 11), the lipoprotein aggregates variously present in the

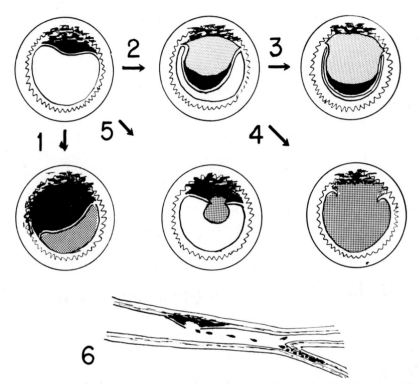

Figure 1. Mechanisms by which the atheromatous plaque may lead to arterial occlusion: the black area represents lipid atheromatous material, the lightly shaded area represents extraluminal blood (hemorrhage), the darker shaded area represents a thrombus. 1) The plaque may grow until the lumen is reduced in size and the blood stream is slow enough to permit local thrombosis. 2) A hematoma may undermine the plaque and 3) finally occlude the lumen, or 4) rupture the plaque intima to leave a ragged ulcer as a basis for thrombosis of the entire lumen. It is possible that even in the absence of hemorrhage, an atheromatous plaque may ulcerate 5) serving as a nidus for thrombus formation or 6) embolizing lipid material into more distal branches where it might also initiate thrombus formation.

plasma perfuse the intima and are ultimately drained away by the venous and lymphatic channels of the media and adventitia of the arterial wall. If the lipoprotein micelles (macromolecules) are unusually large or numerous, or their colloidal dispersion unstable (this peculiarity has not yet been certainly established); or, if the intima by virtue of previous damage leading to local thickness, decreased porosity, or other hindering quality, obstructs the passage of these perfusing micelles; lipoprotein material, or at least the lipids thereof, may be left in the subintima. This is presumed to be a discontinuous process, occurring only at certain times when, for one reason or another, there is a sufficient level of the culpable lipo-proteins in the plasma. A plaque will form and enlarge but the process is reversible in its early stages. This is most likely what happens in the experimental animal. Whether this same process is really self-perpetuating and can go on to arterial occlusion remains in real doubt. Correlation of premortem blood lipid levels with the severity of atherosclerosis at autopsy has not been particularly good, presumably because the duration, as well as the height, of the serum lipid elevation is important. Thus, the atherogenic periods may be intermittent, of varying duration and perhaps remote from the terminal occlusive event.

By this theory, the accelerating effect of an increased intimal perfusion rate in hypertension is readily understood. Local injury, inflammation and mechanical strain effecting the intima must be invoked in this or any other theory to explain the focal nature of the lesions.

Duguid's Theory of Intimal Thrombosis. This has recently gained many adherents in the United Kingdom and on the continent. It attractively combines thrombosis and plaque formation in a modern version of Rokitansky's "Encrustation Theory" first introduced in 1852. Duguid felt that minor injuries to the intima must be constantly occurring and that at each such site a thrombus formed (12). This thrombus may be white or red according to the number of red cells enmeshed in the fibrin clot, large or small in proportion to the magnitude of the injury and perhaps to the clot-ting tendency of the blood at that particular moment. Rather quick-ly the fibrin clot becomes endothelialized. The thrombus then be-comes organized, and the lipid remaining in the resulting plaque is proportional to the residue of red cells. If red cells were at a minimum, a collagenous sclerotic plaque would remain behind; if at a maximum, phagocytes would attempt to remove the lipid com-ponent of the red cell membrane, but because of the difficulty in organization of such a red thrombus "fatty degeneration" would occur to explain the plaque lipid. What contribution unaltered red cell lipid may make to the plaque lipid is not clearly spelled out.

In his original article (13) Duguid showed examples of arteries obviously the seat of repeated thromboses, pointed out their histologic similarity to plaques less obviously thrombotic in origin, and stated that he could find smaller fibrin clots in various states of endothelialization and organization in otherwise normal arteries. Unfortunately, many pathologists doubt that there are such early fibrin lesions. Moon and Rhinehart, in this country, felt that a collagenous degeneration frequently preceded lipid deposition as the earliest lesion (14). Others have felt that a collagenous scar is more often the site of previous lipid deposition successfully cleared, or the site of local injury not involved in lipid deposition at the time of its occurrence (15). Perhaps these lesions are in fact the endothelialized fibrin clot. Attractive as this unification of clotting and atheroma seems, its proof is difficult and it does not explain the development of the experimental lesion. Undoubtedly, thrombi do form, recanalization and endothelialization do occur, but how early and how often in the course of development of the local plaque this may occur is still open to conjecture.

The Hemorrhage Theory. Winternitz originally suggested that the lipid deposits seen in atheromata were the residue of red cells left by local hemorrhage into the subintima (16). This idea has never been generally accepted, but Wartman (8, 17) and Patterson (18), among others, have suggested that hemorrhage into the plaque is a most important factor in the later progress of the disease. Winternitz has amply demonstrated the fact that well developed intimal plaques are supplied with unusually rich capillary invasion at their periphery (19). Blake has even reported finding hemorrhage into the plaques of over 50% of unselected men coming to autopsy over the age of forty-five years (20). It is rather difficult, however, to reconcile the success of anticoagulant therapy, in both the acute and chronic phases of the disease, with the idea that hemorrhage plays a frequent role in morbidity and mortality due to coronary artery disease. On the other hand, factors which promote capillary rupture are poorly understood and again there is only disagreement among pathologists as to how early and how frequently such hemorrhage occurs.

Any theory of atherogenesis must account for diverse observations, not the least of which is the chemical composition of the early atheromatous plaque. The composition of the early plaque varies depending on the material which is deposited, and it is likely that the clue to the atherogenic agent(s) will derive from chemical correlations between the plaque and the etiologies incriminated in the theories just noted.

THE CHEMISTRY OF THE ATHEROMATOUS PLAQUE

Chemical analysis of the atheromatous plaque has largely been concerned with its lipid composition. Unless enzymes in the arterial wall are capable of altering the lipid lodged there, it should be possible to identify the source of the lipid material. For example, the red cell contains virtually no esterified cholesterol; thus, if all of the atheromatous lipid is derived from red cells, there should be only free cholesterol present. If, instead, one or another of the serum lipoproteins are selectively deposited, the free to ester cholesterol ratio, perhaps coupled with the cholesterol/phospholipid ratio, might help to identify the culprits. As will be seen, contamination of the plaques with blood may complicate the picture, nevertheless important clues are now apparent on this point.

Windaus (21) examined two normal and two atherosclerotic aortae for their cholesterol content. The total cholesterol extractable from the whole abnormal aortae was increased more than tenfold, the greater increase being in the esterified cholesterol. Schoenheimer (22) analysed six normal and eight atherosclerotic aortae and found that in the latter there was a tenfold increase in ether soluble materials. He not only confirmed that ester cholesterol increased more than the free, but also observed that their ratio remained about the same in early and calcified plaques; this suggested to him that the calcium of the plaque was not forming soaps with fatty acids liberated in the hydrolysis of the cholesterol esters, else there would have been an increased free cholesterol. Phospholipid was also increased to 3 to 5% of the lipid extract, and small amounts of galactoside and another substance, presumably oxycholesterol, were also isolated.

Meeker and Jobling (23) , Zeek (24) and later Weinhouse and Hirsch (25) examined isolated intimal plaques in various stages of development—early fatty, fibrous, calcified and ulcerated. Though each group may have used slightly different criteria, they did attempt to characterize the individual lesion and to separate the intimal lesion from the media. While there was some increase in lipid content of the intima with age, this was trivial compared to that seen with increasing severity of the lesion. The ratio of ester: free cholesterol seen in early and medium plaques is comparable to that of normal intima (Table I) , though somewhat different than reported by Schoenheimer and Windaus. In the most advanced lesions (ulcerated, large) a trend toward a relative increase in free cholesterol became manifest, so that free and esterified cholesterol occurred in about equal proportions. At the same time the percent of total lipid present as phospholipid fell and the cholesterol/phospholipid ratio increased substantially. While it may be objected that each of these groups worked with only a few specimens, it is rather remarkable that they agreed so well. McArthur (26) confirmed these earlier workers, but, like Schoenheimer, made no effort to study individual graded lesions.

TABLE I

RATIOS OF ESTERIFIED TO FREE CHOLESTEROL AND TOTAL CHOLESTEROL TO PHOSPHOLIPID IN THE ATHEROMATOUS PLAQUES OF THE AORTA

Authors	Ref.	Normal Intima			Medium, Fibrous or Unspecified Plaques			Advanced or Ulcerated Plaque		
		$\frac{EC^+}{FC}$	$\frac{C^{++}}{P}$	n	$\frac{EC}{FC}$	$\frac{C}{P}$	n	$\frac{EC}{FC}$	$\frac{C}{P}$	n
Windaus	21	.354•	—	2	1.29•	—	2	—	—	
Schoenheimer	22	.79•	—	6	1.44•	—	8	—	—	
Meeker & Jobling	23	1.47	1.2	6	1.47	2.8	12	1.01	3.0	15
Zeek	24	0.66	1.6	11	1.86	1.2	7	0.57	2.7	4
Hirsch & Weinhouse	25	1.63	1.9	5	1.57	3.1	5	0.93	3.3	4
McArthur	26	—	—		1.42•	—	1	—	—	
Page	11	—	—		1.30	2.9	2	—	—	
Buck & Rossiter	27	0.34•	0.6•	13	1.40	2.1•	9	0.49	3.1•	8

n=number of aortic lesions studied.

•Full thickness of aorta analyzed: other figures excluded media and adventitia, either by physical separation or appropriate calculation. (Media has EC/FC= 0.57 and C/P=0.57. The media influences results significantly, only in figures for normal intima, or perhaps early plaques (not included in this table)) .

+ In all of these calculations esterified cholesterol (EC) is equal to 0.60 x cholesterol esters, and the ratio of EC/FC is the molar cholesterol that is esterified over that which is free.

++C/P=total cholesterol divided by phospholipid.

More recently Buck and Rossiter (27) have reinvestigated the question of the chemistry of the atheroma. They also analysed the whole aorta wall, but then took pains to compare the grossly diseased part of an aorta with grossly normal segment from the same aorta. The differences between these two values were calculated and presumed to be due entirely to "atheroma lipid." The composition of the "atheroma lipid" was similar to that of the intimal plaque reported by Weinhouse and Hirsch. Its overall percentage of phospholipid and neutral fat was 10% and 30% respectively; the cholesterol:phospholipid ratio was quite high (5.0), somewhat higher than the still later observations of Batchelor (28); the phospholipid was found to be 66% sphingomyelin and 34% lecithin, no cephalin being present. These authors concluded that it was unlikely that these plaque lipids were derived from plasma, which contains only about 15% sphingomyelin and 80% lecithin. This high cholesterol:phospholipid ratio has been difficult to explain for, if indeed lipid were derived from plasma, it must be either highly selected or undergo rather marked chemical transformation.

Fatty acid concentrations in the plaque have recently been studied by Tuna, Recters and Frantz (29) in an effort to test the hypothesis that saturated fatty acids, as the esters of cholesterol or in triglyceride, were selectively involved in plaque formation. Fatty acids of various chain lengths and with one, two or more unsaturated bonds were found in pooled atheromatous plaques with "no qualitative or gross quantitative differences" between the distribution of fatty acids in the plaques and that in normal pooled plasma. While the ratio of linoleic/oleic acid was 1.9 in the plasma and only 1.1 in the plaques, the data prevented any conclusion regarding this finding. More recently, Wright and his co-workers (30) reported on their own and other studies in which this same tendency was noted, but the limitations of their data and a review of still other work did not persuade them that a significantly higher level of saturated fatty acids occurred in the atheromatous plaque than in the plasma.

Many other substances found in plaques have been studied less intensively. Hemosiderin deposits, suggesting vascularity of, if not hemorrhage into, the plaque, have been reported by Patterson (18).

Ceroid, a sudanophilic amber pigment that is insoluble in fat solvents, but extractable by hot alkali, has been found in unusual concentration by Hartroft and his co-workers (10). Blankenhorn (31) has demonstrated substantial quantities of carotenoids in atherosclerotic lesions. Efforts to implicate various connective tissue enzymes and substrates in plaque development have been largely unrewarding.

Addendum: The detailed studies of the lipids of normal and diseased aortae carried out by Böttcher and co-workers (69) of Leiden lend further support to the data presented above and add new refinements to the analyses of fatty acids.

Chapter II

THE SERUM LIPIDS

T HE PREDOMINANCE of lipid in atherosclerotic plaques suggests that either these lipids accumulate by invasion from the blood stream or by local synthesis in the arterial wall. Though the latter occurs, its contribution to plaque lipid is definitely small, making the former mechanism more acceptable (32). Numerous studies have implicated the blood lipids in atherogenesis; it seems reasonable to examine the blood lipoprotein patterns with a view to comparing their chemical relationships with those of the lipid found in the plaque.

Lipoproteins. Lipid is carried in the blood in the form of large multi-molecular aggregates containing principally neutral fats, sterols, phospholipids and protein. They have been described as having a central globule of neutral fat in which may be dissolved free cholesterol and other fat-soluble substances, such as carotene and the other fat-soluble vitamins. This globule is more or less surrounded by a hydrophilic coating of interlaced protein, phospholipid and cholesterol esters which serve to keep the lipoprotein micelle in colloidal state. It has only been in recent years that these lipoproteins have been isolated, categorized and their chemistry studied. Macheboeuf (33) first isolated fat bearing proteins of constant composition from horse serum. Employing Cohn fractionation techniques, Oncley et al. (34) found, in confirmation of earlier studies, a plasma lipoprotein which moved as a beta globulin in the Tiselius electrophoresis apparatus.

McFarland, and then Pedersen, had earlier noted a distortion of the albumen boundary upon centrifuging whole serum: the sedimenting peak of albumen seen on the record of the analytical ultracentrifuge was distorted by a low peak which moved more slowly and was designated "X-protein" (35). This was inconstant in appearance and of uncertain quantitative significance. In 1949 Gofman, Lindgren and Elliott (36) increased the overall density of the serum by adding concentrated salt solution to permit the flotation of a whole series of lipoproteins. The "X-protein" was identified as a lipoprotein. Once isolated from a sample of serum by a preparative centrifugation, the concentration of these buoyant lipoproteins in the supernatant layer could be measured in the analytical ultracentrifuge. Thus, powerful impetus was given to the study of these fat bearing proteins, which are the native form in which fat appears in the blood plasma.

Gofman found that in the serum of rabbits made hypercholesteremic by fifteen weeks of cholesterol feeding there was, in addition to a "normal" lipoprotein which floated at an average rate of 5 to 8 x 10^{-13} cm./sec./dyne/gm. (S_f5-8), a faster floating lipoprotein material (37). Usually, the amount of material in the normal S_f range increased before the abnormal material with flotation rates from 10 to 30 S_f appeared, and it was only when the latter had been present that moderate to severe atherosclerosis appeared in the rabbit arteries. Further studies in his laboratory on human sera convinced Gofman and his co-workers that a similar phenomenon occurred in humans. Human sera had two major lipoproteins which were associated with either alpha or beta globulins. Whereas the concentration of high density alpha lipoprotein did not seem to be influenced, the level of beta lipoproteins (S_f0-10) and of the associated lighter density lipoproteins (S_f10-20 and S_f20-200+) tended to be elevated in patients who had coronary artery atherosclerosis, using the criterion of a previous myocardial infarction, and who had diabetes, nephrosis, xanthomatosis, etc.; diseases known to be frequently complicated by atherosclerosis (38).

Nomenclature of Lipoproteins. The committee on lipid nomenclature of the Society for the Study of Arteriosclerosis has suggested that the terms alpha and beta lipoprotein be reserved for those measurements performed by electrophoresis, regardless of the medium used, and "high density" and "low density" lipoprotein be the respective designations when these same substances are determined in the centrifuge. Unfortunately, there are at least two lipoproteins in the high and two in the low density category, in addition to the largest and lightest particles, the chylomicra. Oncley has designated the two "low density" lipoproteins of human serum the beta lipoprotein and the low-density beta-lipoprotein (39). However, this latter material has been found on zone electrophoresis to migrate as an $alpha_2$ lipoprotein (40, 41). Since this material seems to be distinct from the more predominant beta lipoprotein both chemically and in its response to various agents, it seems worthwhile to distinguish it clearly in the discussions that follow. Hence, we have elected to call this the low-density $alpha_2$ lipoprotein, with the realization that further knowledge may require revision of this term. The relative mobilities of the various lipoproteins on zone electrophoresis and in the ultracentrifuge are shown in the idealized Figure 2.

General understanding in this area has perhaps been hampered by the dictum that identification of the lipoprotein by its density was to be preferred when possible. This developed because of the widespread application of the analytical ultracentrifuge in this field. However, when this tool is used, the lipoproteins can only be identified by density. Since neighboring lipoproteins frequently overlap in this ultracentrifuge, isolated peaks being the exception, their quantitative determination involves integrating the concentrations of lipoproteins between two flotation limits. These limits are designated by flotation rates or negative Svedburg (sedimentation) units (10^{-13} cm./sec./dyne/gm.) under defined conditions of temperature and density of the medium. "S_f" implies that flotation units are determined at a solvent density of 1.063 gm./cm.^{3} and a temperature of 26°C. At other solvent densities a subscript indicating the density used replaces the "f", the temperature must be defined and, since the Svedburg unit (S) is used for sedimentation, a negative Svedburg (-S) is used for flotation: e.g. $-S_{1.21}$. The standard S_f (S_f^o) is discussed on page 126. The two common flotation designations for the aforementioned lipoproteins are also tabulated in Figure 2. Henceforth, we shall use the terminology in the two left hand columns, in conjunction with the nomenclature used by individual experimenters. Note that the low density $alpha_2$ lipoprotein corresponds to Gofman's S_f20-100 and probably encompasses S_f100-400, overlapping, perhaps, with the beta lipoprotein in the S_f10-20 (or $-S_{1.21}$ 40-80) range.

THE CHEMISTRY OF THE LIPOPROTEINS

Heavy density lipoproteins are alpha globulins carrying less neutral fat and cholesterol, but relatively more phospholipid than the less dense beta globulin. The latter is usually isolated with a variable and relatively small amount of low density alpha$_2$ lipoprotein floating before and often blending in the centrifuge with the large major peak of beta lipoprotein but sometimes showing additional peaks overlapping with the huge microscopically visible fat globules called chylomicra (S_f up to 40,000). These lipoproteins vary greatly in density because of varying fat content and are thought to be "metabolized" from the large chylomicra through progressively smaller particles until they became stabilized at some higher density, probably as heavy density lipoproteins. There is still no agreement as to where one should draw the line separating chylomicra from low density alpha$_2$ lipoprotein, if, indeed, they warrant separate consideration.

Low-density alpha$_2$ lipoprotein. Kunkel and Trautman (40) isolated the low-density lipoprotein of density < 1.006 (S_f12-100) which floated just ahead of the beta-lipoprotein (density = 1.035) in the centrifuge. They found that this material had the mobility of alpha$_2$ globulin in zone electrophoresis using starch or a polyvinyl resin (see Figure 2), thus casting doubt upon the earlier designation of this material as a beta lipoprotein. The earlier identification seemed to have a sound basis: the lipoprotein reacted antigenically like beta lipoprotein, it was precipitated by the same ethanol-water systems as beta lipoprotein and metabolic experiments with I[131] labelling suggested a direct relationship between low- and high-density beta lipoproteins (39). Careful scrutiny, however, shows these tests to be too non specific to permit such a definite conclusion.

Dangerfield and Smith (42) employing paper electrophoresis also observed a material moving ahead of the beta lipoprotein which they termed the "pre-beta lipoprotein" and which might conceivably be the same as the low density alpha$_2$ lipoprotein. It was not further identified but did contain about 34% of the total cholesterol (43), and was found to be significantly elevated in patients with coronary disease.

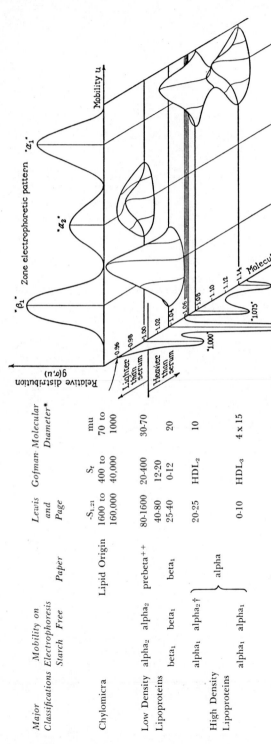

Major Classifications	Mobility on Starch Free Electrophoresis		Paper	Lewis and Page $-S_{1.21}$	Gofman S_f	Molecular Diameter*
	Starch	Free				mu
Chylomicra			Lipid Origin	1600 to 160,000	400 to 40,000	70 to 1000
Low Density Lipoproteins	alpha2	alpha2	prebeta++	80-1600	20-400	30-70
	beta1	beta1	beta1	40-80	12-20	
			beta1	25-40	0-12	20
	alpha1	alpha2†	alpha	20-25	HDL2	10
High Density Lipoproteins	alpha1	alpha1	alpha	0-10	HDL3	4 x 15

* Assuming spherical, hydrated micelles, except when both diameters given.

† This moiety is in low concentration, is reported as having the mobility of an alpha2 globulin on free electrophoresis, of an alpha1 globulin of zone (starch) electrophoresis.

++ Designation of Dangerfield and Smith (42)

Figure 2. Idealized diagram showing the interrelationships between the lipoproteins as analyzed in the ultracentrifugal (flotation pattern) and in zone electrophoresis (mobility) techniques. To the left are the various designations given to the same materials, the terminology arising from different techniques. The material S_f10-20 (or $-S_{1.21}$ 40-80) has no clear counterpart on electrophoresis for this is doubtless an overlapping mixture of the materials from higher and lower S_f bands. The drawing is reproduced from the J. Clin. Investigation (ref. 40), by permission of the copyright owners.

The analysis of the terminal amino acids of the protein of the low density alpha$_2$ lipoprotein gives further support to the notion that it is actually an alpha globulin. From such analyses of various centrifugally isolated fractions the N-terminal amino acid of alpha$_1$ globulin is mainly aspartic acid, and the C-terminal amino acid is threonine; whereas, the beta lipoprotein peptide fraction contains predominantly an N-terminal glutamic acid and C-terminal serine (44). Shore (45) has reported a study in which N-terminal serine and C-terminal alanine peptides appeared in the lipoproteins of density 0.980. The most recent study of this type is that of Rodbell (46), whose results indicate that the protein fraction of the lipoproteins separated in the ultracentrifuge is quite different for the alpha$_1$ (density > 1.063), the beta (density 1.019-1.063), and the chylomicra (Figure 3). The material floating at density 1.006 includes the low density alpha$_2$ lipoproteins and contained a predominant amount of terminal amino acids similar to that of alpha$_1$ lipoprotein.

Beta Lipoprotein. There is little disagreement that the major carrier for lipids is the beta$_1$ lipoprotein (average density, 1.035; diameter, 185Å). It occurs in greatest concentration and is responsible for carrying roughly 60% of the cholesterol in the plasma. While there is a certain inhomogeneity of this material, overlapping as it does with the faster rising low density alpha$_2$ lipoproteins, the protein moiety behaves like beta globulin on all counts so far investigated. While this material is susceptible to dietary and hormonal influences, the changes do not always parallel those of the low density alpha$_2$ lipoproteins or the chylomicra.

Alpha$_1$ Lipoprotein. This appears as two separate peaks in the ultracentrifuge, as is apparent in Figure 2, but travels as one peak in zone electrophoresis. These two components differ largely in the amount of protein they carry, the heavier (average density 1.14; 40 x 150 Å) having almost twice the proportion of protein seen in the lighter (average density 1.09; 100 Å); however, the terminal amino acid analyses suggest no difference in the quality of the protein involved (45). Phospholipid occurs in somewhat greater concentration here than in the beta lipoprotein, as may be seen from the cholesterol/phospholipid (C/P) ratio of 0.5, as compared to

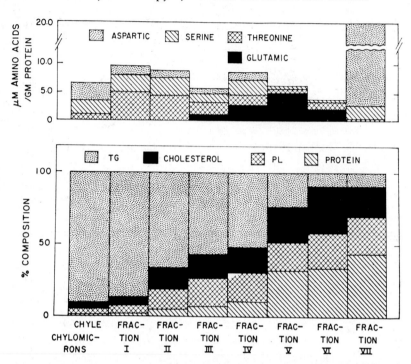

Figure 3. N-terminal amino acid and lipid composition of lipoproteins from chyle and plasma. Chylomicra from chyle were obtained from a patient with chylothorax, Fractions I, II and III are from three patients with essential hyperlipemia, the rest are from pooled plasma. The first 3 fractions represent chylomicra of density less than 1.006. Fraction III corresponds to S_f40-100, IV to S_f20-50, V to S_f10-20, VI to S_f0-10, and VII to the heavy density alpha lipoproteins.

1.3 for the beta lipoprotein. The detailed chemical composition and certain physical constants, insofar as these have been worked out, have been recently reviewed by Oncley (39, 41). Selected lipid ratios derived from these data are seen in Table II and the average proportions of the lipid constituents are present in graphic form in Figure 4.

Recently, the authors have carefully examined the amount of free and esterified cholesterol in the three major subdivisions of the lipoproteins: the $alpha_1$ lipoproteins (density > 1.063), the beta lipoprotein (density 1.063-1.019) and the low density $alpha_2$ lipoprotein (density < 1.019) *. These fractions were separated from individual sera by the centrifugal technique of Havel, Eder and Bragdon (47). Aliquots of each fraction were then extracted in appropriate fat solvents and placed on a column of alumina which allowed complete chromatographic separation and recovery of free and esterified cholesterol, which were determined colorimetrically by a modification of the ferric chloride technique of Zlatkis, et al. (48). The average esterified: free cholesterol ratios (EC:FC) and total cholesterol:phospholipid (TC:PL) ratios for twelve normal subjects can be seen in Table II where they are compared with similar figures derived from the literature (39, 47-57). There is the expected difference in cholesterol:phospholipid ratio between $alpha_1$ and $beta_1$ lipoproteins. In addition, there is a statistically significant difference between the EC:FC ratio noted in the low density $alpha_2$ lipoprotein (density < 1.019), as compared with that of the two fractions of heavier density. This confirms other workers and indicates that the ester:free cholesterol ratio is not the same but does vary significantly among the lipoproteins. Lipoproteins of patients so far studied with coronary disease seem by these parameters to have the same lipoproteins, though the concentration of low density $alpha_2$ lipoprotein (density < 1.019) cholesterol is often found to be elevated.

The cholesterol:phospholipid ratio of the low density $alpha_2$ material shows great variation. While we have confirmed the ratio reported for normal subjects by others, it may become quite high in patients with increased serum concentration of very low density lipoproteins, approaching the data on chylomicra reported by Albrink et al. (56) (Table II).

In summary, five distinct lipoprotein classes have been defined. In order of increasing density and decreasing amounts of neutral fat these are: chylomicra, low density $alpha_2$ lipoproteins, $beta_1$ lipoproteins, and two $alpha_1$ lipoproteins. Though there is some overlapping of these classes when centrifugal isolation is attempted,

---

*The sera were from normal fasting male subjects and contained no visible chylomicra.

TABLE II

RATIOS OF ESTERIFIED TO FREE CHOLESTEROL, AND TOTAL CHOLESTEROL
TO PHOSPHOLIPID IN RED BLOOD CELLS, WHOLE PLASMA AND THE
VARIOUS LIPOPROTEIN FRACTIONS OF HUMAN SUBJECTS

| *Authors* | *Red Blood Cells* | | *Plasma* | | *Authors* | *Chylomicra* | |
Ref. #	$\frac{EC}{FC}$	$\frac{TC}{PL}$	$\frac{EC}{FC}$	$\frac{TC}{PL}$	*Ref #*	$\frac{EC}{FC}$	$\frac{TC}{PL}$
49	0.09	0.49	2.05	0.85	54	1.18	0.96
50	–	–	2.57	0.85	55	3.10	0.73
51	0.00	–	2.65[+]		56	[+]2.00	4.1 (0.9-18.0)[+]
52	–	–	2.30	0.92			
53	–	–	2.17	0.94			

LIPOPROTEINS OF SERUM

| | *L.D. Alpha$_2$* (<1.019) | | *Beta$_1$* (1.019-1.063) | | *H.D. Alpha$_1$* (>1.063 | |
	$\frac{EC}{FC}$	$\frac{TC}{PL}$	$\frac{EC}{FC}$	$\frac{TC}{PL}$	$\frac{EC}{FC}$	$\frac{TC}{PL}$
54	1.61	0.88	3.15	1.35	–	–
57	1.39	0.84	3.20	1.38	–	–
58	1.21	0.86	2.35	1.67	–	–
59	–	–	2.18	1.28	3.9	0.49
41	–	–	2.83	1.08	3.0	0.57
53	1.43	1.11	2.27	1.47•	2.94	0.51

[+] Based on abnormal sera, but excluding liver disease.
• Based upon 7 individual sera.

these lipoproteins differ in the chemical and physical measurements
so far reported and probably in their biological role as well. The
chylomicra carry so much neutral fat that other chemical constituents are still at issue and it is yet uncertain as to whether these
may not be simply fat laden low-density alpha$_2$ lipoproteins. The
latter are distinguished from low density beta$_1$ lipoproteins by their
lesser density, a higher proportion of cholesterol which is free, and
terminal amino acids more suggestive of an alpha than a beta globulin. The beta lipoprotein is quantitatively the principal cholesterol
bearing micelle of the plasma and migrates electrophoretically as
a beta globulin. It has a substantially higher cholesterol: phospholipid ratio than either of the two heavy density lipoproteins. The
latter migrate as alpha globulins and can be separated by differences
in their density and their mobilities on free electrophoresis, if not
on zonal electrophoresis. Apparently, the one of heaviest density
carries twice as much protein as the lighter.

Chapter III

BLOOD LIPIDS, PLAQUE LIPIDS AND
THE INFILTRATION THEORY

THE QUESTION REMAINS whether the atheroma lipid arises from the lipids of the serum by infiltration or from the lipids of the red blood cells, either from an intimal hemorrhage or an endothelialized thrombus. Let us first assume, as have others (11), that no significant decomposition or other chemical change takes place in these lipids, once they are deposited. Weinhouse and Hirsch (25) concluded from their classic study that the proportions of the individual lipid constituents in the plaque corresponded to those of the serum and thus gave great weight to the infiltration theory. They were apparently not concerned by the higher proportion of free cholesterol in plaques as compared to normal serum, but they were puzzled by the still greater proportion in the most advanced plaques, described as "ulcerated." That these changes were undoubtedly real is borne out by their consistent confirmation by other investigators (23, 24, 27). The values for ester:free cholesterol ratios are remarkably uniform for the *uncomplicated plaque* (early lesion) each time these have been reported (Table I) but are substantially different from that of *whole serum* (Table II), as can be seen in Figure 4.

Ester: Free Cholesterol Ratio. An explanation for the differences in this ratio becomes apparent if we study the relative proportions of free cholesterol, esterified cholesterol and phospholipid in the red cell, the whole serum, and the various lipoprotein fractions. The ratio of esterified to free cholesterol in the red cell is extremely low, as there appears to be little if any esterified cholesterol in the red cell (51). Hence, it is difficult to explain the lipid of the atheromatous plaque entirely on the basis of entrapped red cell lipid. On the other hand, if the lipid in the *advanced ulcerated lesions* were modified, as it may frequently be, by a certain proportion of red cell lipid, the average ester:free cholesterol ratio might be expected to fall a corresponding amount, the overall value varying considerably depending upon the red cell contribution. As a matter of fact, Weinhouse and Hirsch (25) describe some of their ulcerated plaques as containing clotted blood. The cholesterol/ phospholipid ratio of the plaques is rather high for any reported constituents of the blood, but particularly for the red cell lipid which has a cholesterol/phospholipid ratio less than (about half) that of whole serum.

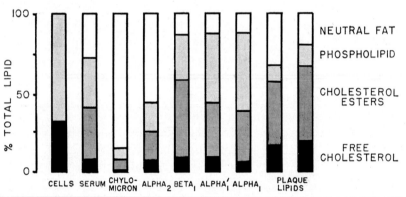

Figure 4. Proportion of various lipid fractions in (left to right) red blood cells; whole serum; chylomicron fraction; low density alpha$_2$, beta$_1$, heavy density (d=1.09) alpha$_1$ (HDL$_2$) and (d=1.14) alpha$_1$ (HDL$_3$) lipoproteins; and in two reports on plaque lipids (Ref. #27 and 25).

Turning now to lipoprotein chemistry, is it possible to find the origin of the plaque lipid in any specific fraction? Values for individual sera do show considerable variation, but average values, from the literature, for esterified/free cholesterol ratios in the three major lipoprotein fractions do agree well (39). The ratio of 1.43 for the low density alpha$_2$ lipoprotein (density < 1.019) agrees surprisingly well with the average value derived from previous investigations on medium or fibrous, or otherwise unspecified, uncomplicated atheromatous plaques.

Phospholipids. The cholesterol:phospholipid ratio for this same type of medium plaque is apparently about 2.5 to 3.0, whereas published values for the low-density alpha$_2$ lipoprotein are about 0.9 (54, 57, 58). The C/P ratio in the normal beta-lipoprotein is about 1.4. Our own data would suggest that this ratio varies widely in the low density alpha$_2$ lipoprotein and is frequently higher in certain individuals than the published values would indicate, sometimes as high as 2.0. This particular point is still being investigated in our laboratory. Perhaps the low phospholipid found in the plaque is due to its more rapid decomposition or loss, or perhaps this is indeed a consequence of the selective mode of lipoprotein deposition in atherogenesis.

Ahrens and Kunkel (60) confirmed the crucial importance of the serum phospholipid in maintaining neutral fat in a dispersed soluble state. With the addition of lecithinase to serum, and the consequent separation of phospholipid and triglyceride, the serum became milky in direct proportion to the total neutral fat present. It is intriguing to speculate whether it may not indeed be just those macromolecules in the alpha$_2$ lipoprotein class which are low in phospholipid, therefore which are less hydrophilic, that are selectively left in the subintima.

On the other hand, perhaps the strongest opposition to the infiltration theory derives from the experiments performed by Zilversmit and his coworkers (61). In a series of acute experiments in rabbits they have demonstrated that six hours after the injection of P$_{32}$ into cholesterol-fed rabbits, the phospholipids extracted from aortae have a specific activity roughly twice as high as those extracted from plasma. This holds equally well for cephalin, lecithin and sphingomyelin, in order of decreasing specific activity. In eviscerated animals, where P$_{32}$ incorporation into plasma phospholipids was reduced by 90 percent, the same high specific activity was still found in the aorta. Other experiments had shown that P$_{32}$ labelled lipoproteins injected intravenously in the rabbit appeared in very low concentrations in the arterial wall. It was implied from these data that the bulk of the phospholipid of the aorta was synthesized within the arterial wall rather than arriving there from plasma perfusion. While exception might be taken to these conclusions on the basis that these findings only pertain to a unique experimental situation, some fundamental questions also remain to be answered.

It was demonstrated in the course of these experiments that

after the six hour period the plasma phospholipid did increase far above plaque phospholipid in specific activity. Little is known concerning the rate of incorporation of P_{32} into the various phospholipids of the plasma, of the individual lipoproteins, or of the aortic intima. Turner et al. (62) reported a three-fold variation among the phospholipids of centrifugally separated lipoproteins in their specific activities; these lipoproteins were not further characterized, but they were thought to encompass "a very active system" of "phospholipid unassociated with cholesterol." The possibility remains that one lipoprotein incorporates P_{32} faster and at the same time happens to selectively perfuse the intima. Even if there is a lipoprotein in the aortic wall which incorporates P_{32} faster than plasma phospholipids in the first few hours of exposure, it is not yet established that this active phospholipid is necessarily correlated with atherogenesis.

More compelling perhaps is the finding of Buck and Rossiter (27), mentioned above, (page 110) who found a difference in the proportions of cephalin, lecithin and sphingomyelin of the plaque lipid, as compared with the plasma lipids. Phillips (63) has reported upon the relative proportions of these phospholipids in the various lipoproteins; except for the sphingomyelin concentration, which was about twice as much in beta as in alpha$_1$ lipoproteins, they did not vary much among the various lipoproteins. To conserve the infiltration theory, it must then be postulated that phospholipids are lost from the developing plaque. Other data do suggest that cephalin is the most active and sphingomyelin the least active in their rate of turnover in the aorta (64). Thus we would expect little or no cephalin, some lecithin, and much sphingomyelin in atheromatous aortae. If the sphingomyelin were all brought to the aortic plaque by plasma lipoproteins, and never removed, the cholesterol:sphingomyelin (C:S) ratio should be the same in both places. Employing the figures of Buck and Rossiter, the C:S ratio of plaque lipid would be 3.1 to 4.5; the C:S ratio in the low density alpha$_2$ would be roughly 3.9. This provides a feasible alternative explanation for the low level of plaque phospholipid reported.

Triglycerides. The neutral fat (triglyceride) content of the lipid extract of the plaques (Figure 3) is reported to be in the neighborhood of 26%, if galactosides are included in the calculation. This falls between the value for the low density alpha$_2$ lipoprotein (d=0.98) of 55% and that for the principal beta-lipoprotein (d=1.035) of 12%. Again the average value for neutral fat in the former is based on a very few observations on presumably normal sera, and from the broad range of flotation values included, this must also encompass considerable variations in the proportion of neutral fat.

Plaque Lipoproteins. Recently Hanig (65) has been able to make saline extracts of normal and atherosclerotic aortic intimas. By studying the ultracentrifuge pattern, he was able to demonstrate a recovered lipoprotein of the low-density variety (S_f12-100) from the atherosclerotic lesions. Furthermore, none of the other lipoprotein species of serum could be recovered at all from any aortae, and none of these low density lipoproteins from normal aortae. However, a greater element of protein was present in the tissue lipoprotein than is seen in serum lipoprotein, and further chemical comparisons need to be made. In a somewhat similar study, Batchelor (28) extracted lipoproteins from atherosclerotic aortae and found, in addition to a high cholesterol/phospholipid ratio (1 to 3.0), a protein uniquely soluble in zinc salt solution under conditions which would normally precipitate serum lipoprotein.

THE COOPERATIVE STUDY OF LIPOPROTEINS
AND ATHEROSCLEROSIS

The "Cooperative Study." Gofman's observations aroused such interest the nation over that in 1952 the United States Public Health Service undertook a cooperative effort involving four laboratories and many individuals to pursue a large scale study of the comparative value of the serum cholesterol concentration as opposed to the concentration of the band of lipoproteins S_f12-100 in the prediction of new coronary disease in the adult male population aged forty to fifty-nine. Great efforts were required to finally standardize the techniques employed in the study and establish agreement among the laboratories, but finally large numbers of healthy men had their serum tested with the knowledge that a few would inevitably develop clinical disease.

Midway in the study, Gofman recognized that he was not getting the clean cut results he had noted earlier and attributed this to the fact that there had been a change in technique: this was undertaken to enhance its accuracy, but had actually complicated the calculations. Five milliliters of serum were being used for the initial preparatory centrifugation instead of three; thus, though a greater amount of the lipoprotein S_f12-100 was available for analysis, there was, by the same token, a much greater concentration of the major beta lipoprotein (S_f8). By virtue of a cohesive effect, first noted by Johnston and Ogston (66), this tended to slow down the flotation rate of the S_f12-20 lipoprotein, so that much of it tended to appear in the S_f0-12 category. Without dwelling further on the importance of this change, suffice it to say that the decision was made in the cooperative study not to make the calculations required to correct for the Johnston-Ogston effect. Thus, it is not hard to understand why two divergent conclusions were reached: the cooperating laboratories provided the bulk of the data and concluded that the serum cholesterol provided as accurate a prediction of future trouble from coronary atherosclerosis as did a measurement of the S_f12-100 lipoproteins; the Donner laboratory group concluded that, if allowance be made for the magnitude of beta-lipoprotein concentration $(S_f0$-12), a statistically significant improvement over the serum cholesterol determination could be demonstrated. To accomplish this, they measured the "atherogenic index," which is the sum of weighted values of not only the corrected ("standard") $S_f^\circ12$-20 and $S_f^\circ20$-100, but also "standard" $S_f^\circ0$-12 and $S_f^\circ100$-400 lipoproteins. It did provide a better prediction, though the improvement in biological significance was not impressive (67).

It was unfortunate that this cooperative study was performed prematurely, not only because difficulty arose in determining the most desirable techniques to use, but also because of the unsettled state of knowledge concerning the rest of the lipoprotein spectrum in the atherogenic process. The S_f12-20 lipoprotein is but an arbitrary fraction of the lipoprotein spectrum, and probably includes overlapping beta and low density alpha$_2$ lipoproteins. By also including S_f20-100, the low density alpha$_2$ lipoprotein was analyzed, but the chylomicra and the beta lipoproteins were largely ignored by the cooperating laboratories.

If it is true that certain lipoproteins of the serum are, in fact, responsible for plaque formation, could these lipoproteins have been measured by the laboratories involved in "The Cooperative Study" even though they did not obtain more clear-cut evidence in support of this concept? In the first place, we know that a very large proportion of men in this country, and in the age range studied, are well on their way to clinical coronary artery disease. Hence, to use the population at large as a basis for "normal" will permit no easy separation of those whose lesions have progressed to the point of clinical symptoms. It could permit only a statistically significant separation wherein the total population being compared with the affected population, is greatly diluted by many, probably well over 50%, whose arteries will be at least equally involved by atherosclerosis. It was concluded by the majority report that "the difficulty of demonstrating an association of serum lipids with atherogenesis may be related to the inappropriate use of an American population, which is almost universally affected with atherosclerosis" (67).

Secondly, in the use of their criteria for atherosclerosis we find many complexities. Atherosclerosis was deemed to have been present (or to have been developing), at least more so than in the rest of the population under study, in those men who later developed new coronary incidents—fresh onset of "angina pectoris, coronary thrombosis, myocardial infarction, peripheral vascular disease, cerebrovascular accident and sudden death." As we have pointed out earlier (chapter I), virtually all of these symptoms mean an accidental occlusion, usually by thrombosis, which episode may be related to entirely different serum lipid factors having different time constants than are involved in the development of the plaque (see page 104). About all that could really be concluded from this study was the fact that the serum cholesterol and the S_f12-100 (low density alpha$_2$) lipoprotein are equally weak as predictors for development of new thrombotic episodes.

In essence the epidemiological approach can provide us with only limited information relating serum lipid levels to the development of atherosclerosis, as long as new thrombotic catastrophes are used as the major index of the disease in life. This is true because other lipid factors may also be involved in the thrombotic process to cloud the issue, because probably plaque formation and certainly thrombosis are discontinuous, intermittent processes; and because there exists no good way of selecting a satisfactory control group. In contrast, chemical comparisons of human lesions with certain lipo-proteins would seem to provide increasingly persuasive evidence for the infiltration theory, and may represent a most productive ap-proach in establishing the etiology of atherosclerosis.

Summary. As we review the analysis of the lipids of the athero-sclerotic plaque and compare the more recently reported chemical constitution of the lipoproteins with that of the plaque, we still find ample support for the time honored infiltration theory of atherogenesis. However, we must postulate selective deposition of particular lipoprotein species which are lighter and larger than the normal beta lipoproteins and which may in fact carry an $alpha_2$ rather than a $beta_1$ globulin. The normal beta lipoprotein is in a fairly stable dispersion and is perhaps a small enough particle to pass through the intimal interstices, whereas the chylomicron may be too large: it is the intermediate material that is under appropriate conditions deposited. It should be noted, however, that some workers consider it likely that these low density $alpha_2$ lipoproteins are derived from those of still lower density, perhaps including the chylomicra (68).

Early observers noted the fact that the ester:free cholesterol ratio of the plaque lipid (1.4) was lower than the normal serum value of roughly 2.5, but found that it did agree fairly well with that of hyperlipemic plasma. The decline in this ratio with the most advanced lesions has never been explained, but is a consistent find-ing in each series studied. This is perhaps explained by the fact that such ulcerated plaques must be variously involved in some degree by thrombosis or hemorrhage with consequent entrapment of red cell lipid which is virtually free of any esterified cholesterol. This would correspond equally well for thrombosis on the plaque, or hemorrhage into the plaque, and apparently neither occurs except in the most advanced and complicated lesions.

The ratio of ester:free cholesterol is remarkably similar in the plaque lipid and in the low density $alpha_2$ lipoprotein of the serum. The proportion of neutral fat is variable in this lipoprotein, but comparable also with that in the plaque. The extremely low phospholipid content of plaque lipids has been seen in the low density alpha₂ lipoproteins of certain individuals, but a selective loss of certain phospholipids is perhaps a more feasible explanation for this finding. Finally, the atheroma lipid when suspended in saline has the same density in the centrifuge as this lipoprotein. These similarities, plus many observations in experimental animals, provide compelling evidence that this lipoprotein present in the serum of many humans is responsible for the initiation of the atherosclerotic plaque. Whether this particular lipoprotein is deposited because of colloidal instability, and whether a paucity of phospholipid or a surfeit of saturated fatty acids are additional prerequisites to atherogenesis, is not known. The answers to these questions await further work before the low-density alpha₂ lipoprotein can be considered as the only established atherogenic element of the plasma. It must be remembered that we have been speaking only of plaque formation, not vascular occlusion, and that the data pertain to the aorta—to the coronary arteries only by inference. Nevertheless, the infiltration theory, modified by selective lipoprotein deposition and phospholipid escape, still seems to explain most of the observed facts better than the Duguid or Winternitz theories of plaque formation. The latter are useful to explain the later changes in the advanced lesions which are undoubtedly important considerations in significant proportion of cases of thrombosis and occlusion.

REFERENCES

1. Boyd, W.: *Pathology for the Physician.* 6th. Edition, Lea and Febiger, Phila., 1958.
2. Gould, S. E.: *Pathology of the Heart.* 1st. Edition, Charles C Thomas, Springfield, Ill., 1953.
3. Moritz, A. R.: Medionecrosis aortae idiopathica cystica. Am. J. Path., *8:* 717, 1932.
4. Ponseti, I. V., Wawzonek, S., Shepard, R. S., Evans, T. C., and Stearns, G.: Further Studies on Lathyrism in the Rat. Proc. Soc. Exper. Biol. & Med., *92:* 366, 1956.
5. Blumgart, H. L., Schlesinger, M. J. and Davis, D.: Studies on the Relation of the Clinical Manifestations of Angina Pectoris, Coronary Thrombosis and Myocardial Infarction to the Pathologic Findings. Am. Heart J., *19:* 1, 1940.

6. Roberts, J. C., Moses, C. and Wilkins, R. H.: Autopsy Studies in Atherosclerosis. Circulation, *20:* 511, 520, 527, 1959.
7. Yater, W. M., Traum, A. H., Brown, W. G., Fitzgerald, R. P., Geisler, M. A. and Wilcox, B. B.: Coronary Artery Disease in Men Eighteen to Thirty-Nine Years of Age. Am. Heart J., *36:* 334, 481, 683, 1948.
8. Wartman, W. B.: Vascularization and Haemorrhage in the Arterial Wall. *Studies in Pathology* presented to Peter MacCallum: University Press, Melbourne, 1950.
9. Snow, P. J. D., Jones, A. M. and Daber, K. S.: A Clinico-pathological Study of Coronary Disease. Brit. Heart J., *18:* 435, 1956.
10. Hartroft, W. S. and Thomas, W. A.: Pathological Lesions Related to Disturbances of Fat and Cholesterol Metabolism. J. A. M. A., *164:* 1899, 1957.
11. Page, I. H.: Some Aspects of the Nature of the Chemical Changes occurring in Atheromatosis. Ann. Int. Med., *14:* 1741, 1941.
12. Duguid, J. B.: Pathogenesis of Atherosclerosis. Lancet, *2:* 925, 1949.
13. Duguid, J. B.: Thrombosis as a Factor in the Pathogenesis of Coronary Atherosclerosis. J. Path. and Bact., *58:* 207, 1946.
14. Moon, H. D. and Rhinehart, J. F.: Histogenesis of Coronary Arteriosclerosis. Circulation, *6:* 481, 1952.
15. Wilens, S. L.: The Nature of Diffuse Intimal Thickening of Arteries. Am. J. Path., *27:* 825, 1951.
16. Winternitz, M. C., Thomas, R. M. and LeCompte, P. M.: *The Biology of Arteriosclerosis.* Charles C Thomas, Springfield, Ill., 1938.
17. Wartman, W. B.: Factors other than Cholesterol in Atherosclerosis. Minnesota Med., *38:* 749, 1955.
18. Patterson, J. C.: The Reaction of the Arterial Wall to Intramural Hemorrhage. Pg. 65. Symposium on Atherosclerosis. Publ. #338 National Acad. Sci.—National Res. Council. 1955, Washington 25, D.C.
19. Winternitz, M. C.: The Blood Supply of the Vessel Wall. Idem. pg. 14.
20. Blake, T. M.: Intramural Hemorrhage in Coronary Arteries. Circulation, *16:* 496, 1957.
21. Windaus, A.: Uber den Gehalt Normaler und Atheromatöser Aorten an Cholesterin und Cholesterinestern. Z. für physiol. Chem., *67:* 174, 1910.
22. Schoenheimer, R.: Zur Chemie der Gesunden und der Atheros-

klerotischen Aorta . . . Z. für physiol. chem., *160:* 61, 1926 and idem. *177:* 143, 1928.

23. Meeker, D. R., and Jobling, J. W.: A Chemical Study of Arteriosclerotic Lesions in the Human Aorta. A.M.A. Arch. Path., *18:* 252, 1934.

24. Zeek, P. M.: A Chemical Analysis of Atherosclerotic Lesions in Human Aortas. Am. J. Path., *12:* 115, 1936.

25. Weinhouse, S. and Hirsch, E. F.: Chemistry of Atherosclerosis: I. Lipid and Calcium Content of the Intima and of the Media of the Aorta with and without Atherosclerosis. A.M.A. Arch. Pathol., *29:* 31, 1940.

26. McArthur, C. S.: The Acetone-soluble Lipid of the Atheromatous Aorta. Biochem. J., *36:* 559, 1942.

27. Buck, R. C. and Rossiter, R. J.: Lipids of Normal and Atherosclerotic Aortas: Chemical Study. A.M.A. Arch. Path., *51:* 224, 1951.

28. Batchelor, W. H.: Lipoproteins in the Arterial Wall. pg. 212 in The Symposium on Atherosclerosis. Publ. #338. National Academy of Sciences—National Res. Council. 1955, Washington, D. C.

29. Tuna, N., Rectors, L. and Frantz, I. D. Jr.: Fatty Acids of Normal Plasma and Arteriosclerotic Plaques. J. Clin. Invest., *37:* 1153, 1958.

30. Wright, A. S., Pitt, G. A. J. and Morton, R. A.: Cholesteryl Ester Fatty Acids and Plasma. Lancet, *2:* 594, 1959.

31. Blankenhorn, D. H. and Braunstein, H.: Carotenoids in Man. III. The Microscopic Pattern of Fluorescence in Atheromas, and its Relation to their Growth. J. Clin. Invest., *37:* 160, 1958.

32. Gould, R. G.: Sterol Metabolism and Its Control. Pg. 100. Symposium on Atherosclerosis. Publ. #338 National Academy of Sciences—National Research Council. 1955, Washington, D.C.

33. Macheboeuf, M. A.: Recherches sur les Phosphoaminolipids et les Sterides du Serum et du Plasma Sanguins. Bull. soc. chim. biol., *11:* 268, 483, 1929.

34. Oncley, J. L., Gurd, F. R. N. and Melin, M.: Preparation and Properties of Serum and Plasma Proteins. XXV Composition and Properties of Human Beta-Lipoprotein. J. Am. Chem. Soc., *72:* 458, 1950.

35. Mann, G. V.: A Short History of Lipoproteins. pg. 7 in *The Lipoproteins: Methods and Clinical Significance.* S. Karger, Basel, Switzerland, 1958.

36. Gofman, J. W., Lindgren, F. T. and Elliott, H. A.: Ultracentrifugal Studies of Lipoproteins of Human Serum. J. Biol. Chem., *179:* 973, 1949.

37. Gofman, J., Lindgren, F., Elliott, H., Mantz, W., Hewitt, J., Strisower, B. and Herring, V.: The Role of Lipids and Lipoproteins in Atherosclerosis. Science, *111:* 166, 1950.

38. Gofman, J. W., Jones, H. B., Lindgren, H. T., Lyon, T. P. Elliott, H. A. and Strisower, B.: Blood Lipids and Human Atherosclerosis. Circulation, *2:* 161, 1950.

39. Oncley, J. L.: The Lipoproteins of Human Plasma Pg. 14 in *The Lipoproteins: Methods and Clinical Significance*. S. Karger, Basel, 1958.

40. Kunkel, H. G. and Trautman, R.: The Alpha$_2$ Lipoproteins of Human Serum: Correlation of Ultracentrifugal and Electrophoretic Properties. J. Clin. Invest., *35:* 641, 1956.

41. Oncley, J. L. and Gurd, F. R. N.: The Lipoproteins of Human Plasma. Pg. 347 in *Blood Cells and Plasma Proteins*. Academic Press. N. Y., N. Y., 1953.

42. Dangerfield, W. G. and Smith, E. B.: An Investigation of Serum Lipids and Lipoproteins by Paper Electrophoresis. J. Clin. Pathol., *8:* 132, 1955.

43. Besterman, E. M. M.: Lipoproteins in Coronary Artery Disease. Brit. Heart J., *19:* 503, 1957.

44. Avigan, J., Redfield, R. and Steinberg, D.: N-Terminal Residues of Serum Lipoproteins. Biochem. Biophys. Acta., *20:* 557, 1956.

45. Shore, B.: C- and N-Terminal Amino Acids of Human Serum Lipoproteins. Arch. Biochem. and Biophys., *71:* 1, 1957.

46. Rodbell, M.: N-Terminal Amino Acid and Lipid Composition of Lipoproteins from Chyle and Plasma. Science, *127:* 701, 1958.

47. Havel, R. M., Eder, H. A. and Bragdon, J. H.: The Distribution and Chemical Composition of Ultracentrifugally Separated Lipoproteins in Human Serum. J. Clin. Invest., *34:* 1345, 1955.

48. Zlatkis, A., Zak, B. and Boyle, A. J.: A New Method for the Direct Determination of Serum Cholesterol. J. Lab. and Clin. Med., *41:* 486, 1953.

49. Foldes, F. F. and Murphy, A. J.: Distribution of Cholesterol, Cholesterol Esters and Phospholipid Phosphorus in Normal Blood. Proc. Soc. Exp. Biol. and Med., *62:* 215, 1946.

50. Peters, J. P. and Man, E. B.: The Interrelations of Serum Lipids in Normal Persons. J. Clin. Invest., *22:* 707, 1943.

51. Brun, G. C.: Cholesterol Content of the Red Blood Cells in Man. Acta Med. Scand. Suppl., *#99:* 1–237, 1939.
52. Boyd, E. M.: Species Variation in Normal Plasma Lipids Estimated by Oxidative Micromethods. J. Biol. Chem., *143:* 131, 1942.
53. Cohen, L., Batra, K. V. and Jones, R. J.: Studies on the Total, Ester and Free Cholesterol of Serum and Serum Lipoproteins. Unpublished.
54. Bragdon, J. H., Havel, R. J., and Boyle, E.: Human Serum Lipoproteins. I. Chemical Composition of Four Fractions. J. Lab. and Clin. Med., *48:* 36, 1956.
55. Laurell, C. B.: Preliminary Data on the Composition and Certain Properties of Human Chylomicrons. Scand. J. Clin. Lab. Invest., *6:* 22, 1954.
56. Albrink, M. J., Man, E. B., and Peters, J. P.: The Relation of Neutral Fat to Lactescence of Serum. idem., *34:* 147, 1955.
57. Oncley, J. L., Walton, K. W. and Cornwell, D. G.: A Rapid Method for Bulk Isolation of Beta-Lipoproteins from Human Plasma. J. Am. Chem. Soc., *79:* 4666, 1957.
58. Lindgren, F., Nichols, A. V. and Freeman, M. K.: Physical and Chemical Composition Studies on the Lipoproteins of Fasting and Heparinized Serum. J. Phys. Chem., *59:* 930, 1955.
59. Hillyard, L. A., Entenman, C., Feinberg, H. and Chaikoff, I. L.: Lipid and Protein Composition of Four Fractions Accounting for Total Serum Lipoproteins. J. Biol. Chem., *214:* 79, 1955.
60. Ahrens, E. H. and Kunkel, H. G.: The Stabilization of Serum Lipid Emulsions by Serum Phospholipids. J. Exper. Med., *90:* 409, 1949.
61. Zilversmit, D. B.: Phospholipid Turnover in Atheromatous Lesions. Page 145 *Hormones and Atherosclerosis,* edited by G. Pincus, Academic Press Inc., N. Y., N. Y., 1959.
62. Turner, R. H., Snavely, J. R., Randolph, M. L. and Goldwater, W. H.: Some Peculiarities of the System of Serum Lipoproteins which Contain Phospholipids but no Free Cholesterol. Tr. Ass. Am. Physicians, *65:* 94, 1952.
63. Phillips, G. B.: The Phospholipid Composition of Human Serum Lipoprotein Fractions Separated by Ultracentrifugation. J. Clin. Invest., *38:* 489, 1959.
64. Smith, E. B.: The Phospholipids in the Human Aorta. Biochem. J., *73:* 34P, 1959.
65. Hanig, M.: Prediction of Atherosclerosis by Lipoproteins. In *The*

Lipoproteins: Methods and Clinical Significance. S. Karger, Basel, 1958.

66. Johnston, J. P. and Ogston, A. G.: Boundary Anomaly Found in Ultracentrifugal Sedimentation of Mixtures. Tr. Faraday Soc., *42:* 789, 1946.

67. Gofman, J. W. et al.: Evaluation of Serum Lipoprotein and Cholesterol Measurements as Predictors of Clinical Complications of Atherosclerosis. Report of a Cooperative Study of Lipoproteins and Atherosclerosis. Circulation, *14:* 691, 1956.

68. Lindgren, F. T., Nichols, A. V., Hayes, T. L., Freeman, N. K. and Gofman, J. W.: Structure and Homogeneity of the Low-Density Serum Lipoproteins. Ann. N. Y. Acad. of Sciences., *72:* 826, 1959.

69. Böttcher, C. J. F., Woodford, F. P., TerHaar Romeny-Wachter, Boelsma-Van Houte and Van Gent, C. M.: Fatty Acid Distribution in Lipids of the Aortic Wall. Lancet *1:* 1378, 1960.

SECTION IV
SERUM LIPID ALTERATIONS

Chapter I

DIETARY

How IMPORTANT it may be to reduce any particular element of the serum lipids is not known. This is in part because we are not certain which of the serum lipid elements is responsible for the manifestations of atherosclerosis; in part because a cause and effect relationship between serum lipid elevation and coronary disease is not established; and these uncertainties exist because the course of coronary atherosclerosis is so unpredictable. Gofman found, after his initial hypothesis had been well advanced, that, while a strong correlation existed between clinical coronary disease and the serum level of $S_f^o12\text{-}400$ (low density alpha$_2$) lipoproteins, a correlation also existed, if somewhat weaker, with the $S_f^o0\text{-}12$ or beta lipoprotein. Hence, he introduced the concept of the "atherogenic index" which made allowance for the relative importance which he felt these lipoprotein categories deserved in the prediction of future manifestations of coronary disease (1). Since these correlations were not of a very high order, and these two lipoproteins do include the bulk of the serum cholesterol, it has been easy to accept the finding that the carefully determined serum cholesterol is no worse than a lipoprotein determination for predictive purposes (2). Though it is tempting to speculate on the therapeutic implications, it remains uncertain whether a reduction of the serum cholesterol, or any other lipid, will favorably influence the progress of the disease.

Without waiting for a definitive answer to this complex problem, many investigators, including the authors, have been exploring the effects of diet, hormones, and other agents upon the serum lipid levels. Most often, because of the relative ease and reliability of its measurement, the serum cholesterol has been followed serially in a group of patients (or animals) on one or more treatment regimens with more or less information concerning the effects upon the individual lipoproteins. Two reports (3, 4) on the long term benefits of serum lipid reduction upon the course of this capricious disease have been enthusiastic, but the difficulties in interpretation are not insignificant. At any rate, let us examine the various efforts to influence the serum lipids. For excellent exhaustive reviews relating nutrition and the serum lipids, or atherosclerosis, the reader is referred to those by Ahrens (5), Katz and Stamler (6), Portman and Stare (7) and Gofman (8). Several recent symposia on agents effecting serum lipids (9-13) must also be recommended.

Let us concern ourselves with the role of natural dietary elements. The phytosterols (in edible vegetables), cerebrosides (in meat), and nicotinic acid are common elements of the diet. However, they must be used in greater than the usual dietary quantities to have a significant effect upon the serum lipids; hence, their discussion is reserved for a later chapter.

STEROLS

Cholesterol. This ubiquitous animal sterol (see Figure 1), has been an important factor in the dietary production of atheromatous lesions in a great many animal species ever since Anitschkow's feeding of cholesterol to rabbits in 1905. This led to the logical conclusion that the cholesterol of the diet should be restricted.

Keys and his coworkers (14) demonstrated in a large group of Twin City business and professional men that the serum cholesterol had no correlation with dietary cholesterol level as derived from a dietary history. In dietary surveys in Sardinia and in controlled experiments they found that widely varying dietary cholesterol intakes (200 to 1200 mg./day) were not reflected in the serum cholesterol level. Recently, this conclusion has been challenged by Beveridge (15). He found in a two week experiment in men that the serum cholesterol was dependent upon the dietary level. This can hardly be considered as overthrowing the previous data, in view of the experiments of Shull et al. (16) in dogs. This suggested that while the level of cholesterol in the diet did determine the rate of ascent of the serum cholesterol, it did not determine its ultimate level on chronic feeding, which depended rather on other elements of the diet. These observations have been confirmed by the authors in the rat. Thus, in short experiments one might find early differences in the serum cholesterol level, according to its level in the diet, which would not persist. The habitual level of dietary cholesterol in most populations is probably not the main dietary determinant of the serum lipid pattern (7, 14, 17) .

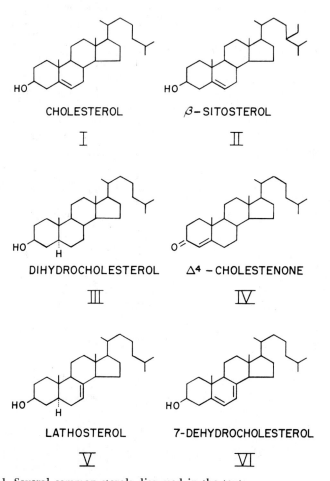

Figure 1. Several common sterols discussed in the text:
    I. Cholesterol (Cholest-5-en-3β-ol)
   II. β-Sitosterol (24b-ethylcholest-5-en-3β-ol)
 III. Dihydrocholesterol (5α-cholestan-3β-ol) , see figure 2, section I.
  IV. Δ4-cholestenone (cholest-4-en-3-one)
   V. Lathosterol (5α-cholest-7-en-3β-ol)
  VI. 7-dehydrocholesterol (cholesta-5:7-dien-3β-ol)

Other sterols are of interest in passing: Δ 4-cholestenone, lathosterol (Δ 7-cholestenol), dihydrocholesterol (cholestanol) and 7-dehydrocholesterol (see Figure 1) are all readily absorbed. Δ 4-cholestenone (IV) was of interest because it provoked marked suppression of cholesterol synthesis. Presumably the enzymatic pathway was competitively utilized to convert Δ 4-cholestenone (IV) to cholestanol (III) which then accumulated in the liver and in arterial plaques (18). This followed the observations that the feeding of cholestanol (III) competitively inhibited cholesterol (I) absorption. However, about 50% of the cholestanol was absorbed and induced a cholestanol atheromatosis in chickens (19) and in rabbits (20).

FAT

The Level of Dietary Fat. Keys and Anderson (17) have reviewed the mass of evidence which supported the idea that the higher the fat level in the diet, the higher the serum cholesterol. Serum cholesterol reduction was consistently observed when individuals were placed on the rice diet of Kempner, on a fat free diet of protein hydrolysate and dextrimaltose, or even on diets where the daily intake of fat was reduced by only 25 gm. In earlier studies, it didn't seem to matter whether animal fat or vegetable fat was used, but it was not appreciated that hydrogenated vegetable fats might differ in effect from the original unsaturated vegetable oil. In addition, there may have been instances akin to our female patient (vide infra) who showed a dramatic fall in serum cholesterol level on simple hospitalization. At any rate, subsequent work has shown that the quality of the dietary fat is a more important parameter than its total level. The reason that the level of fat in the diet of various groups does correlate so well with averaged serum cholesterol therein is because most of the differences in dietary fat levels are due to differences in intake of the saturated fats of meat and dairy products.

Unsaturated vegetable oils. Kinsell's group found that substitution of vegetable oils for animal fats in the diet had a striking effect on the serum cholesterol (21). These original observations were confirmed and extended by Beveridge (22, 23), Ahrens

(5, 24, 25) and their coworkers. These reductions in serum cholesterol concentration were dramatic in the case of corn, cottonseed,
peanut and safflower oils and chicken fat; were intermediate with
palm and olive oils, lard and beef fat, which contain fewer double
bonds and therefore have a lower iodine number; and were least
with cocoa butter, coconut oil and butter which usually induced a
cholesterol level 30 to 60% higher than that seen in the same subject
on corn oil (25). As long as a single oil was consumed, the subject's cholesterol level remained constant, his plasma triglycerides
and ultimately all the bodies' fat depots approached the fatty acid
composition of the ingested oil. The general structure of a triglyceride, or neutral fat, may be seen in Figure 2, along with several
fatty acids found in natural food triglycerides.

FATTY ACIDS

I STEARIC

$CH_3(CH_2)_{16}COOH$

II OLEIC

$CH_3(CH_2)_7CH = CH(CH_2)_7COOH$

III LINOLEIC

$CH_3(CH_2)_4CH = CHCH_2CH = CH(CH_2)_7COOH$

IV LINOLENIC

$CH_3CH_2CH = CH(CH_2CH = CH)_2(CH_2)_7COOH$

V ARACHIDONIC

$CH_3(CH_2)_4CH = CH(CH_2CH = CH)_3(CH_2)_3COOH$

TRIGLYCERIDE

(R = FATTY ACID)

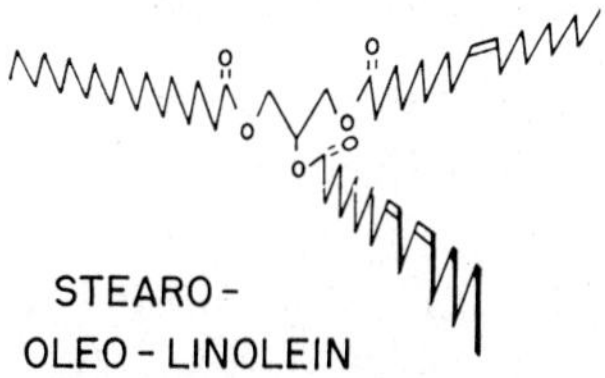

STEARO -
OLEO - LINOLEIN

Figure 2. Naturally occurring neutral fats are represented by the general triglyceride structure in the upper right, which contains a combination of three fatty
acids (R). A perspective representation of the triglyceride stearo-oleo-linolein
is seen in the lower right. The commoner C-18 and C-20 fatty acids are listed
on the left.

Is the vegetable oil substitution supplying a positive suppressive
effect upon the serum cholesterol level, or is there some "noxious"
property to animal fat, as Gofman has suggested (26), which somehow provokes a rise in serum lipid levels? Is the effect of saturated

fats merely due to their lack of enough double bonds, or is it due to a relative deficiency of a particular essential fatty acid, especially the dienoic 20-carbon linoleic acid? Or could it be due to a deficiency of certain phospholipids, plant sterols, or some as yet unidentified plant factor? The bulk of the evidence pretty well excludes factors other than the fatty acids (5, 6, 7), and interesting formulae have been worked out which relate the serum cholesterol level to certain proportions of various fatty acids. For example, in a series of human experiments in which fats containing varying proportions of saturated and unsaturated fatty acids were isocalorically exchanged, Keys et al. (27) demonstrated that in one group of subjects: the change in serum cholesterol =

2.68 (percent sat. f.a.) − 1.23 (percent linoleic acid) (r = 0.97)

Hegsted et al. (28) from a large series of experiments with rats on cholic acid and cholesterol regimens with various proportions of unsaturated fatty acids, concluded that:

Log serum cholesterol =

3.21 − 0.28 x Log (% linoleic acid x % saturated f.a.) (r = −0.94)

Here the non-essential unsaturated fatty acids (e.g. oleic acid and eleostearic acid) were left out of the equation, inasmuch as they drove the serum cholesterol level up. Keys, on the other hand, considered that oleic and similar fatty acids had no effect, whereas, the saturated fatty acids provoked a rise and the unsaturated linoleic acid provoked a fall in serum cholesterol. The difference between the two formulae is more apparent than real. It must also be appreciated that the animal experimenters used cholic acid supplementation which might obscure any effect of these fats on the enterohepatic bile acid cycle.

Of great interest is the recent observation of Ahrens et al. (29) who reported upon the cholesterol reducing effect of Pilchard oil. This fish oil, when harvested at the proper time, has large amounts of linolenic and arachidonic fatty acids, with relatively small amounts of oleic and linoleic acid. In comparison with corn oil, Pilchard oil maintained equivalently low levels of serum cholesterol in human subjects. This would seem to show that linoleic acid is not the specific agent of this effect. The general conclusion would seem to be that the saturation of the fat, as measured by its iodine number, is the best index to its hypercholesteremic effect. Ahrens et al. (30) demonstrated why such a formulation will fit the data and formulae of Keys, et al.

One other parameter which may modify the effect of unsaturation is chain length. Vegetable oils contain C_{18} and C_{20} fatty acids, whereas the fats which elevate serum cholesterol, butter and coconut oil, are rich in C_4 to C_{14} fatty acids. Cocoa butter has the same amounts of linoleic and oleic acids as are found in corn oil but is richer in C_{16} and C_{18} acids. In spite of these considerations, the weight of evidence would suggest that, while chain length may somehow modify the effect upon serum lipids of saturation of the fatty acid molecule, the influence of the latter is predominant.

The mechanism of action. There is no consistent effect of different fatty acids upon cholesterol synthesis *in vitro,* and variable effects are reported *in vivo* (5-7). While dietary fat seems to be necessary and differences in chain length and degree of intestinal hydrolysis appear to be facilitating factors in cholesterol absorption, the degree of saturation of the fatty acids involved plays a doubtful role (5, 7). The degree of unsaturation of the ingested fat does, however, determine the fecal end products of cholesterol.

In rats, Wilson and Siperstein (31) showed little difference between the effects of corn oil and lard upon excretion of cholesterol, coprostanol and cholestanol; however, a striking increase in non-digitonide precipitable sterols (3 α-hydroxy sterols?) occurred with corn oil. In more acute studies, Byers and Friedman (32) found that continued ingestion of an unsaturated oil, as contrasted with a saturated fat, produced a higher level of chylous cholesterol, but lower levels of serum cholesterol and greater biliary excretion of cholesterol and bile acids.

In one hypercholesteremic human subject, Hellman et al. (33) studied the effect of a formula diet containing first 40% butter, then 40% corn oil, upon serum cholesterol specific activity and the excretory rate of intravenously administered 4-C^{14} cholesterol. Fecal cholesterol and coprostanol accounted for about two-thirds of the recovered radioactivity, the remainder was found in "acidic material, presumably derived from bile acids." Estimates of the cholesterol necessarily lost from the serum with the change to corn oil in the diet agreed quite well with the increase in fecal sterol recovery during that same period. They found no change in the daily output of fecal bile acids. However, Haust and Beveridge (34) were able to demonstrate in ten subjects a substantial increase in fecal excretion of bile acids when they were shifted from a butter to corn oil diet. Goldsmith et al. (35) also observed in six human subjects that the isocaloric substitution of unsaturated for saturated fats produced an increase of 20-25 percent in bile acid excretion and a moderate increase in sterol excretion in the feces.

Four healthy young male students were followed on our metabolic ward for several weeks while on a constant repetitive diet in which levels of saturated animal fat were altered. A level of 150 gm. of fat per day was observed for at least six weeks, then fat was exchanged isocalorically for 100, 75 or 50 grams of carbohydrate (exclusively sugar). Virtually all of the fat was of animal origin and crystalline cholesterol was added to maintain cholesterol intake equal in the two periods. One long six day collection of feces was made for each subject while on the high level and again while on a low level of animal fat. The feces were analysed by techniques to be described elsewhere (36). The serum cholesterol level fell dramatically when the fat level was reduced by even 25 gm. per day; simultaneously there was always an increase in excretion of bile acids, if not consistent differences in sterol excretion, as may be seen graphically in Figure 3.

The evidence would seem to suggest that any reduction of serum cholesterol occasioned by a reduction in the diet of saturated fat, whether or not poly-unsaturated fats are substituted, is accompanied by an increased fecal excretion of bile acids and/or sterols. The lack of effect on the bile acid excretion observed by Hellman et al. may have been because the patient was not a normal subject; or, more likely, other ancillary factors such as intestinal motility, bacterial flora, etc. may ultimately determine cholesterol catabolism—i.e. the proportion that will be disposed of as bile acids or as sterol.

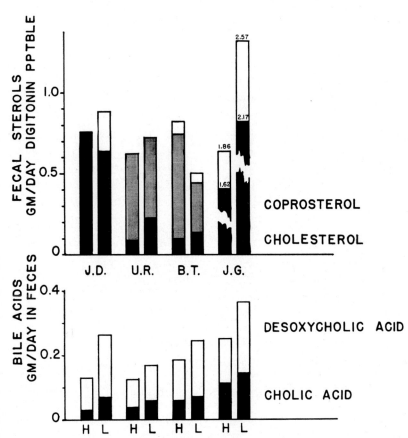

Figure 3. Fecal sterol excretion in four normal subjects on high (H) and low (L) levels of dietary animal fat. Upper array: The height of each bar indicates the total digitonin precipitable sterol recovered in the feces, the black portion represents cholesterol (Lieberman-Burchard positive, digitonin-precipitable material after acetylation of the isolated sterol), and the shaded portion coprosterol or 5β-coprostan-3β-ol (Lieberman-Burchard negative digitonide after acetylation). Lower array: bar height represents the sum of desoxycholic and cholic acid recovered from extracted feces by the chromatographic technique of Abell et al. (ref. 127). In each subject the left hand bar indicates recovery while on a high animal fat diet (150 gm./day), the right hand bar indicates that while on 100 or 75 gm. of fat per day. In the case of J. G. 50 gm. of corn oil was added to the reduced animal fat level (100 gm.) during the second period, hence the increased recovery of sterols, largely phytosterols, during that period.

CARBOHYDRATE

A point which hardly needs emphasis is the fact that one cannot vary the level of one major foodstuff (e g., fat) isocalorically without varying at least one other. In most studies, protein and calories were held constant and fat has been increased or decreased in exchange for carbohydrate. Hatch et al. (37) observed that patients who went on Kempner's rice diet, while they had a substantial fall in serum cholesterol and in S_f0-12 (beta) lipoproteins, actually had a rise in S_f20-100 (low density alpha$_2$) lipoproteins. Ahrens (5) in one of his experiments wherein the dietary level of corn oil was changed from 40% (and 45% carbohydrate) to 10% (and 75% carbohydrate) noted only a slight rise in the serum levels of cholesterol and phospholipid, but the neutral fat level more than doubled. It is perhaps pertinent that in his clever review of national dietary intakes correlated with mortality rates from coronary disease, Yudkin found a much better correlation between coronary disease mortality and the rate of consumption of refined sugar than with the consumption of animal or total fat (38). Limited data of others have also suggested that coronary disease patients consume more carbohydrate than their controls (39).

Recently Gofman (26) has presented data on five subjects which indicate that, while the S_f^00-20 (beta) lipoproteins vary directly with the level of saturated fats in the diet, the S_f^020-400 (low density alpha$_2$) lipoproteins vary directly with the carbohydrate intake. Conversely, the S_f^00-20 lipoproteins were uninfluenced by the carbohydrate level, the S_f^020-400 were unaffected by changes in saturated fat. The drop in serum cholesterol reported earlier by Beveridge on transferring his experimental subjects from a fat free diet to a diet containing 60% corn oil (23) could, it was pointed out, be easily explained by a consequent fall in these cholesterol-poor lipoproteins.

This is an extremely important observation, if our hypotheses from the previous section prove to be correct. Placing patients on a low fat diet for coronary disease might only drive them to eating a larger proportion of carbohydrate and thus elevate their low density alpha$_2$ lipoproteins which contribute to plaque formation. These observations must be confirmed and extended, but there seems to be little doubt that strenuous elevation of carbohydrate can lead to a rise in the level of the lipoproteins carrying large amounts of neutral fat.

The mechanism of this carbohydrate effect is not known, and the relative importance of starch versus sugar and other forms of carbohydate has not been studied in regard to this lipoprotein effect. However, Portman (40) has demonstrated that in rats biliary bile acid excretion was lower in animals on an artificially constructed diet containing sucrose or glucose than on one containing starch as a carbohydrate source. Furthermore, the cholesterol level of the serum of starch fed rats was lower than that of sucrose fed rats, and the difference could be abolished by adding an intestinal antibiotic (7). Here again we see the serum cholesterol varying with bile salt excretion which is influenced by a dietary factor, and perhaps by the intestinal flora; yet this hardly explains how an excess of carbohydrate in the diet leads to the increased formation of one kind of lipoprotein and an excess of fat to another.

PROTEIN

Quality. Since the classical studies of Best and his coworkers of 30 years ago, it has been known that methionine or choline deficiency (aggravated by cystine feeding) would lead in animals to a fatty liver, in which case the serum lipids usually became low. Methionine, lysine or threonine were protective against this fatty liver and restored the serum lipids to normal. It was rather surprising, then, when Mann and his coworkers (41) demonstrated that high serum lipids developed in monkeys (and later rats) maintained on a synthetic diet containing alpha soy protein (with ample choline) and could be restored toward normal by the addition of methionine or by substituting casein for alpha protein as the protein source. This was all the more interesting because atheromatous lesions developed in monkeys maintained on this diet for four to six months. That a dietary deficiency of this sulfur containing amino acid might explain some instances of hypercholesteremia in humans does not seem to be the case, for these same workers could induce no change in cholesterol level of the serum by administering methionine to a fairly large number of individuals (42).

Efforts in our laboratory (unpublished data), as well as those of others, to find some other amino acid imbalance which might influence cholesterol metabolism in the experimental animal have been relatively unrewarding (6, 43). In general, the changes that are seen can usually be attributed to a decrease in total dietary intake of foodstuffs including fat.

Quantity. A more cogent question has been the possible role that protein intake might play, inasmuch as the amount of animal fat and animal protein usually correlate in naturally selected diets. Filios and his coworkers found in rats fed various levels of casein with cholic acid, cholesterol and corn oil that the serum cholesterol varied inversely with the protein level (or directly with the carbohydrate level) (44); whereas, one of us has reported that serum cholesterol levels of rats on less drastic (casein-lard) diets became abnormally elevated when the casein level fell below about 9% or rose above 25% (45). A less dramatic, but definite, elevation has also been seen in younger rats on high casein diets (and now less cholic acid) by the Boston group (46).

In short term studies with growing chickens, there is a linear protective effect against hypercholesteremia and atheromatous lesions with increasing levels of protein up to 35% (47). At low levels of protein (and, of course, high carbohydrate), the S_f20-400 was quite high, and this became proportionately lower on increasing levels of protein (decreasing carbohydrate). The S_f0-20 did not change significantly. This suggests a carbohydrate effect, though Stamler et al. (48) have provided some evidence in similar studies to contradict this idea.

In Man. Keys and Anderson (49) fed diets containing equal fat and calories to schizophrenic subjects at two different levels of protein and found that, for a given level and type of fat, the serum cholesterol level remained the same, regardless of changes in dietary level of protein within the range of 8 to 20 percent of the calories.

In our laboratory two normal male students hospitalized for purposes of dietary control were maintained on eucaloric, constant, repetitive diets, so that no weight change occurred. The diets contained 0, 45, 90 or 135 grams of meat protein which was added to a basic 45 grams of dairy protein (eggs and milk). Protein of vegetable origin was negligible. The carbohydrate included a fixed 90 grams per day of starches plus the remainder, which varied inversely with the protein, from sugars both natural and refined. Thus, the only variables in four dietary periods of approximately 6 weeks each were meat protein and sugar.

TABLE 1

SERUM LIPID CHEMISTRIES IN TWO NORMAL MALE SUBJECTS
ON VARYING DIETARY PROTEIN LEVELS[**]

Protein Intake	No. det'ns.	Mgm.% Total Serum Lipid ±S.D.		Mgm.% Serum Phospholipid ±S.D.		Mgm.% Serum Cholesterol ±S.D.	
gm./d	A/B	A[•]	B[+]	A	B	A	B
ad lib	3/3	678 ± 76	843 ± 87	188 ±25	225 ± 9	156 ±75	211 ±10
45	8/8	552 ±120	819 ± 62	127 ±20	167 ±24	118 ±18	168 ±13
90	9/4	513 ± 40	700 ±116	133 ±12	158 ±10	102 ±13	175 ± 8
135	5/10	564 ± 74	870 ± 56	125 ±18	200 ±22	138 ±17	155 ±14
180	7/7	531 ± 79	799 ± 68	166 ±12	160 ±15	104 ± 9	171 ±22
Corn Oil[†]	7/3	454 ± 66	633	105 ±10	162 ±14	94 ± 9	172 ±24

[•]Subject A weighed 67 kg. and consumed 2560 calories/day.

[+]Subject B weighed 74 kg. and consumed 3060 calories/day.

[**]Diets were repetitively constant and eucaloric throughgout. 90 gm./day of fat were derived almost exclusively from animal fat, and cholesterol intake was constant at 1.1 gm./day. Protein was derived principally from beef (57%) and chicken breast (43%).

[†]A corn oil supplement of 50 gm./day was included in the diet at the expense of sugar.

The results of serum lipid analyses, performed by techniques previously described (50), during each of these four dietary periods may be seen in Table 1. It can be seen that there is no apparent trend in any of the serum lipid parameters measured over this four-fold variation in protein level. Note also how the substantial fall in total lipids on transferring from the high fat ad lib diet to the experimental diet was reflected in a·similar fall in cholesterol and phospholipid, but, in replacing sugar by corn oil, the change in total lipid was much more dramatic than in the other two parameters measured. This is consistent with Gofman's findings (26). Our limited data cover a wider range of protein levels, (7 to 28% of calories) than did that of Keys and Anderson, but still support their conclusion.

The order of these dietary periods varied with each subject so that fortuitous changes in lipid levels with season and quarterly exams might tend to cancel out. It is perhaps worthy of note that

A, who was a below average student, had his highest serum cholesterol level on 135 grams per day of protein during the last weeks of
the school quarter when exams were given. This is interpreted as
an example of anxiety influencing the serum lipids (see page 149).

Mechanism. The explanations for the various effects of protein
feeding upon lipid metabolism are entirely speculative. It is well
known that protein is a potent choleretic, and this raises the possibility that an effect upon the enterohepatic cycle of the bile salts
may again be involved here (45). In view of the important effects
of a diet deficient in the sulfur-containing amino acids, it has also
been postulated that their restriction may limit the production of
taurine, necessary for conjugation with the bile acids to form tauro-
cholate salts, and thus lead to plasma cholesterol retention (7).

TOTAL CALORIES

In all of the studies reported above one or another element of
the diet was varied while calories were kept constant and, except
in experiments with growing animals, at a level to avoid a positive
or negative caloric balance. The converse of an old clinical observation that the cholesterol level falls in a subject in negative caloric
balance has recently been documented by Anderson et al. (51). The
serum cholesterol rose 20 mgm.% on a positive caloric balance of
660 calories per day, reaching a plateau after five weeks. Walker
et al. (52) demonstrated an acute rise in serum cholesterol and
lipoprotein levels in two subjects briefly fed a low fat, high carbohydrate diet of 5000 calories. Mann et al. (53) further showed that,
if heavy physical exertions could elevate caloric expenditure to the
level of the increased intake, the serum lipids returned toward
normal.

Walker and his coworkers had shown earlier that weight reduction led to a fall in both serum cholesterol and beta lipoproteins
(S_f0-13) (54) and Gofman (26) has again shown recently that on
a simple weight reduction regimen both S_f^o0-20 (beta) and S_f^o20-400
(low density alpha$_2$) lipoproteins fall. He suggests that with a weight
reduction diet, since both carbohydrate and fat are restricted, both
groups of lipoproteins fall. This illustrates another difficulty in this
whole area; most investigators concern themselves with the relative

proportions of foodstuffs, and the parameter often used is the percentage of total calories rather than the absolute quantity of a particular foodstuff. It has recently been suggested that perhaps the absolute intake of fat, carbohydrate or protein is the more valuable correlate (39).

Another interesting aspect of the caloric problem is the relationship between OBESITY and the serum lipid levels. References may be quoted to show either that the serum cholesterol level is higher, or that it is lower, in the obese than in the lean man. In view of the sensitivity of the serum lipids to caloric balance, it is quite easy to understand this: most obese people go through cycles of positive and negative caloric balance depending upon a great many factors, some of which may operate in anticipation of a visit to the doctor. The group studied might be predominantly in negative caloric balance or not, depending upon the circumstances. The truest picture was probably obtained in the large Framingham study, where no significant relationship could be established between obesity and serum cholesterol level (55).

Chapter II

HUMORAL EFFECTS UPON SERUM LIPIDS

Recent review articles (11, 12, 56, 57) and a symposium on Hormones and Atherosclerosis (13) comprehensively cover the hormonal and other humoral influences on the serum lipids. In this section we will confine the discussion to those effects upon the serum lipids induced by estrogens, thyroid hormones and "clearing factor." Chemically related compounds or analogues which exert equivalent effects upon the serum lipids have been used experimentally in the unfulfilled hope of avoiding the less desirable effects on target organs.

ESTROGENS

One of the most significant facts about coronary disease in America is the great sex differential that occurs before the age of 40. Women are all but free of the disease until after the menopause and the incidence of the disease then lags about ten years behind that among men until after sixty. This has prompted the studies of the effect of estrogens upon the serum lipids and upon the experimental lesions.

In 1949, Eilert, of this institution, first presented the dramatic effect of estrogen (Estinyl) upon the serum lipids of pre- and post-menopausal women. In her final publication (58) each of twenty cases demonstrated a fall in the serum cholesterol level while phospholipid levels rose, so that the cholesterol/phospholipid ratio fell without a significant change in total lipids. These findings have received ample support from the work of Barr, Russ and Eder (59) and Oliver and Boyd (60). The former showed that young women carried a lower level of beta lipoprotein and of cholesterol than men, in spite of a higher alpha$_1$ lipoprotein. As we have seen, the alpha$_1$ lipoprotein is richer in phospholipid than the beta lipoprotein, hence the lower cholesterol/phospholipid ratio seen with estrogen activity.

Furthermore, while implantation of estrogen pellets into the cockerel has been reported to produce hyperlipemia, with elevated serum cholesterol and subsequent aortic atheromatosis (61), Pick et al. (62) observed that the coronary arteries of such animals were virtually free of lesions. Estrogens seemed to selectively protect against experimental coronary atherosclerosis in the cholesterol-fed chick, and the study of many synthetic compounds in the chick has demonstrated that the coronary protective effect always fell off with the loss of estrogenic effect (63).

In numerous reports, the serum lipids of myocardial infarction survivors have been normalized by estrogen administration, which elevated the $alpha_1$ and reduced the beta lipoprotein levels, usually with some reduction in the overall serum cholesterol and total lipid. According to Gofman (8), $S_f^0 20\text{-}400$ (low density $alpha_2$) lipoproteins are also reduced. These serum changes are sustained as long as this class of hormone is administered, but unfortunately tender enlargement of the breasts, loss of libido, impotence and mental depression occur so frequently that few men have cared to pursue this type of treatment for a significant time. Neither an androgen-estrogen combination nor any estrogen analogue so far studied in man has successfully influenced serum lipids without demasculinizing side effects (64-66).

Mention must be made of an ambitious program, instigated by Stamler et al. (66), attempting to alter the ultimate course of coronary disease, in survivors of a *bona fide* myocardial infarction, by the long-term administration of conjugated equine estrogens (premarin). In an interim report, four years after beginning the study, a carefully matched group of patients carried on a placebo had a "drop-out" rate of 15%, whereas the treated group had 38% "drop-out" due to the above mentioned undesirable side effects. When data for the first twelve months of treatment were examined, no significant benefit of estrogen was apparent in the survival rates. For those patients followed over three years there was a slight advantage; if deaths in the first two months were ignored, a significant improvement in survival rates could be achieved. A high mortality rate due to cardiovascular-renal disease and recurrence of myocardial infarction in these first two months on the large dose of estrogens counteracted the good later results.

It is obvious that we cannot reach a conclusion with regard to the value of estrogen therapy in coronary artery disease. The effects upon the serum lipids are salutary. A beneficial effect upon the course of the disease has not yet been demonstrated in men; though, on autopsy, there is a more advanced degree of atherosclerosis in ovariectomized women than in women with ovaries (67). There remains the hope that the organic chemist may yet provide an estrogen-like compound able to feminize the serum lipoprotein pattern, without feminizing the secondary sex characteristics.

THYROID HORMONES

Perhaps because of the regular elevation of the serum cholesterol in myxedema, it has often been stated that hypothyroidism, like diabetes, nephrosis, xanthoma tendinosum and xanthoma tuberosum, aggravates or promotes atherosclerosis. However, the evidence for this relationship has been reviewed (68, 69) and this conclusion found to be based upon tenuous evidence indeed. Myxedema occurs in the older age group, where a high incidence of atherosclerosis is to be expected; hyperthyroidism at a younger age and in the favored female sex, in the main.

Furthermore, in the definitive reviews of autopsy data on 106 collected cases of cretinism (70) and over fifty cases of primary myxedema (71), both made before the treatment by thyroid extract was introduced, neither the frequency nor severity of atherosclerosis was considered remarkable. Of several case histories often quoted to support this relationship, there were none without a complicating hypertension or nephritis. Production of myxedema in the experimental animal is not consistently effective in promoting atherosclerosis (72). All we can safely conclude is that the evidence is rather weak for a greater intensity of atherosclerosis in human myxedema.

The Serum Lipid Pattern. Figure 4 shows the serum lipid pattern contrasted in twenty-five hyperthyroid and seventeen hypothyroid patients reported by the authors (73). A consistently high serum cholesterol level was observed in the latter, and a frequently low level in the former as observed by others (74, 75). A substantial difference was seen between the levels of total lipid, total cholesterol, phospholipid and beta lipoproteins (-$S_{1.21}$ 20-70), but no significant difference occurred in the alpha$_1$ lipoprotein (-$S_{1.21}$ 0-10). Perhaps because of more advanced age and more cardiovascular complications in the older hypothyroid group, occasional instances of high levels of the low density alpha$_2$ lipoproteins (-$S_{1.21}$ 100-400) were seen; yet 40% of the hyperthyroid patients also had appreciable levels of this same group of lipoproteins. Whatever reservations may be deserved in relating atherosclerotic disease to hypothyroidism, there can be no doubt that the thyroid hormone exerts dramatic effects upon the serum lipids, principally the beta lipoprotein.

When a group of coronary disease patients, matched with regard to sex, age and serum cholesterol level were compared with

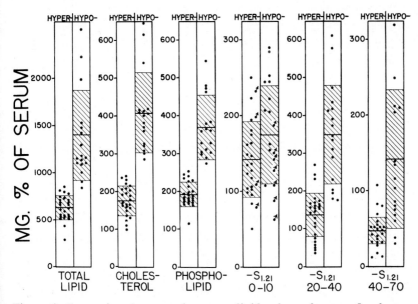

Figure 4. Comparison between the serum lipid values of twenty-five hyperthyroid and seventeen hypothyroid patients. Scattergrams for the concentrations of total lipid, cholesterol, phospholipid and the various lipoprotein fractions, measured ultracentrifugally at a density of 1.21. The sex of the male patients is indicated by the attached arrow in the alpha$_1$ lipoprotein bar (-$S_{1.21}$ 0-10), where sex hormones may exert some influence. The shaded portion of the bar represents one standard deviation on either side of the mean. See ref. 73.

the seventeen hypothyroid patients, with regard to these parameters, the only statistically significant differences occurred in the
beta lipoprotein ($-S_{1,21}$ 20-40) level and in the beta:alpha ratio.
These results indicate that coronary disease patients of equivalent
sex, age, and cholesterol level will have, relative to myxedema patients, a higher level of beta lipoproteins; or conversely, that the
beta lipoprotein in hypothyroidism may be richer in cholesterol
than is that of coronary disease. This returns to the question of
just how much qualitative differences in lipoproteins may be missed
by simple density analysis.

The Mechanism of the Thyroid Effect. Rosenman, Friedman
and Byers (76) have demonstrated that the output of cholesterol
in the bile is abnormally low in hypothyroid and increased in
thyroid-treated rats. Erickson (77) has further shown that this is
paralleled by the bile acids excreted in the bile. Isotopic tracer
techniques also suggest that cholesterol synthesis is increased in
hyperthyroidism and decreased in myxedema (78) . Thus it appears
that hyperthyroidism induces an increased rate of excretion (as
bile acids and sterols) and synthesis of cholesterol, and a low serum
cholesterol; with hypothyroidism these processes are reduced to
subnormal rates and an increased level of serum cholesterol results.

Administration of Thyroid Hormone. Effects upon the serum
lipids of thyroid exhibition have recently been studied by Strisower,
et al. (79-81) in groups of schizophrenic patients. The dosages used
were several times the usual replacement dose in athyreotic subjects
and weight loss, agitation and other manifestations of hyperthyroid
states did occur. At first they observed the same "escape" toward
normal in the serum lipids noted by others, but later experience
showed that, if the dose were large enough, an escape from the lipid
effects did not regularly occur. Interestingly enough, they found
that the main effect upon the lipoproteins occurred in the S_f^o0-20
(beta) lipoprotein, no consistent reduction occurring in the low
density alpha$_2$ (81) .

Oliver and Boyd reported the application of triiodothyroacetic
acid in graduated doses in twelve euthyroid angina patients (82).
A substantial reduction in serum beta lipoprotein cholesterol occurred without producing any elevation in basal metabolic rate.

Nevertheless, three of the patients developed an increased frequency of anginal attacks. They concluded that, like thyroid hormone or thyroxine, this preparation was cardiotoxic and unsafe for use in patients with coronary atherosclerosis, and justifiably discouraged the use of these thyroactive compounds. Recently, however, interest has been kept alive by reports, such as that of Rawson, et al. (83) demonstrating great differences in activity of various chemical analogues of the thyroxine molecule in various *in vitro* test systems. The effects upon tadpole metamorphosis, prevention of goiter development in thiouracil fed rats, and the rate of growth of a thyroid-hormone-dependent tumor transplanted in thyroidectomized mice varied several-fold, even several hunderd fold, one with another. Tri-iodothyropropionic acid as well as triodothyronine was thought to lower cholesterol, without an equivalent effect upon metabolic rate.

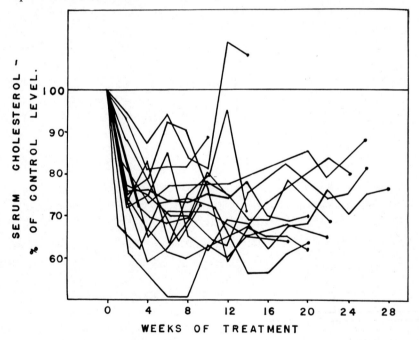

Figure 5. Hypocholesteremic effect of 4 to 8 mgm./day of sodium d-thyroxine in fifteen subjects. Each line represents the serial cholesterol determinations in one subject expressed as percent of the average control level during the preceding six month period (100 percent line).

D-thyroxine. After the enthusiastic report of Starr et al (84), we were persuaded to explore the effects of sodium d-thyroxine in twenty euthyroid patients with coronary atherosclerosis and/or hypercholesteremia on whom adequate pretreatment serum cholesterol values were available (85). The changes in the serum cholesterol, measured every two weeks, may be seen in Figure 5 for fifteen of these patients. No definite trend to "escape" back to the control level was noted for six months, and a mean reduction of 27% in serum cholesterol level was accomplished. The phospholipid was reduced less significantly than the cholesterol of the serum (Figure 6) and the total lipid least of all, supporting the observation of Strisower et al. (81).

The increased calorigenic effect at these dosages was considerable (174 calories per day). Intensification of the anginal syndrome was noted in three patients, aggravation of the symptoms of congestive failure and sudden death were each seen once on the 8 mgm. dose in this series.

Eleven patients on long term dicumarol therapy sustained wild fluctuations in biweekly prothrombin time determinations during the first few weeks of the medication requiring alteration in dicumarol dosage. Fortunately, no bleeding episodes occurred and reestablishment of a steady prothrombin time was usually accomplished. No reverse effect was noted on withdrawal of the drug.

There is abundant evidence from *in vitro* and *in vivo* animal experiments that the dextro-isomer of thyroxine is from 1/3 to 1/10th as potent as the levo isomer in calorigenic effect (86). Tapley and coworkers (87) have demonstrated with isotopically labelled dextro- and levo-thyroxine in the rat striking differences in distribution of the two isomers. D-thyroxine was about twice the concentration of L-thyroxine in the liver and kidney, whereas it appeared in only 1/6th the concentration of L-thyroxine in all other tissues at the same time. This was explained by an excretion rate about three times as great for d- as for l-thyroxine. The d-thyroxine was less completely bound to protein (butanol extractable) and was less of a caloric stimulant on *in vitro* heart and diaphragm O_2 consumption than was l-thyroxine. It was concluded that intestinal absorption, organ distribution and perhaps cell membrane penetrance were different in these two forms (as with other thyroxine analogues) by virtue of the isomeric difference in the side chain. Here again we see those principles at work which were observed with the digitalis glycosides. And again, the hope wanes that separation of calorigenic and lipid effects can be found in a synthetic thyroxine analogue.

HEPARIN AND THE CLEARING FACTOR

In 1943, Hahn (88) first observed that the injection of heparin intravenously led, in the dog, to an abrupt decrease in the usual turbidity of the plasma seen after a fatty meal. The addition of

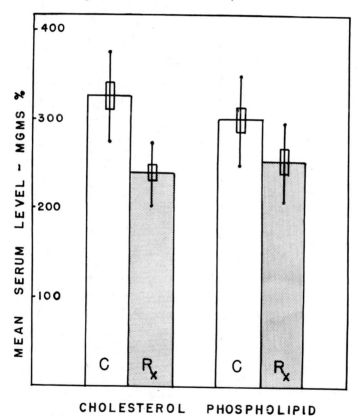

Figure 6. Bar graph comparing the mean levels of serum cholesterol and phospholipid during control (C) and treatment (R) periods up to three months on 4 to 8 mgm./day of sodium d-thyroxine. The small rectangle bisected by the top of the bar indicates the standard error of the mean; the vertical line, one standard deviation.

heparin to lipemic plasma *in vitro* produced no such effect. However, the addition of post-heparin (non-lipemic) plasma to lipemic plasma *in vitro* led to a loss of turbidity, and, under the microscope, dissolution of the visible globules of fat (chylomicra). Many other types of hyperlipemia (nephrosis, rat pregnancy, essential hyperlipemia, CCl_4 poisoning, etc.) have been shown to respond also to this clearing factor, and currently many artificial fat emulsions are employed as substrates in assaying the rate of "clearing" (89). From the first, no change was induced in the concentration of total lipid, cholesterol, or phospholipid of the blood; there was a reduction in neutral fat which could quantitatively account for an increase in free fatty acids and glycerol.

Lipoprotein Lipase. Korn (90) observed that ammonia or serum extracts of acetone-extracted rat heart powder contained this same lipolytic activity, and, like clearing factor, this material specifically hydrolyzed the neutral fat of lipoproteins, hence the term "lipoprotein lipase." Like the clearing factor, lipoprotein lipase will not hydrolyze triglyceride emulsions without a small amount of a fatty acid acceptor (calcium, globulin or albumin) and, in contrast to pancreatic lipase, the rate of hydrolysis is inhibited by bile salts. While the identity of lipoprotein lipase and clearing factor is not conclusively established (57), it seems quite likely that they are the same material (90).

Clearing factor occurs in Cohn's fraction III (beta globulin), where its activity can be concentrated fourteen times over post-heparin plasma (91), and it can be precipitated with the euglobulins. It may arise from many tissues on the injection of heparin and has been recovered in the perfusate after isolated perfusion of heparinized plasma through an extremity, the lungs, the skin and subcutaneous tissue, and, except for the liver, the abdominal viscera (57). Lipoprotein lipase has been prepared from rat, beef and pig hearts, and adipose tissue of the rat and rabbit. It has been extracted in but low concentrations, if at all, from liver, kidney, spleen, skeletal muscle and lung. Since clearing factor is found concentrated in adipose tissue, it is presumed to be a lipolytic enzyme acting in the fat depots. It is released by the injection of heparin and contains heparin, and hence is considered to be a heparin-protein complex which hydrolyzes the triglycerides of the low density lipoproteins (and chylomicra) in the presence of a co-protein acceptor.

Clearing Factor and the Lipoproteins. It was found that simple triglyceride emulsions responded to purified clearing factor or lipoprotein lipase only after they were "activated" by small amounts of an alpha globulin (90), which combines with the neutral fat globule and effectively converts it to a lipoprotein. Lindgren et al. (92) showed, in extension of previous work, that, upon incubating the S_f^o20-400 (low density alpha$_2$) lipoproteins with clearing factor, newly formed high density lipoproteins (HDL$_2$ + HDL$_3$ and perhaps HDL$_1$) could be isolated. Thus, the alpha$_2$ globulin laden with neutral triglyceride (S_f20-400) apparently loses its neutral fat by hydrolysis, until it reverts to a heavy density lipoprotein. Thus, alpha globulins are found in both the "core" of chylomicra and low density lipoproteins. They also suggested that a similar loss of glyceride occurred within the S_f4-20 (beta) lipoprotein, leaving a "core" of HDL$_1$ lipoprotein (92), but other workers have not confirmed this (93).

Electrophoretic studies showed that *in vivo* effects of heparin upon protein mobilities were profound. The mobility of both alpha and beta globulins is increased, a portion of the alpha globulin band even migrating ahead of the albumin peak. Since heparin carries such a strong negative charge many of these changes must be interpreted with caution, but a pre-albumin band, seen only after clearing of lipemic serum, undoubtedly represents the alpha globulin modified by the association of newly liberated free fatty acids (94).

The Specificity and Physiological Importance of Heparin. Clearing of lipemic plasma may also be provoked by many heparinoids, dextran sulfate, treburon, paritol C., and many other sulfated polysaccharides. Non-sulfated compounds such as phosphorylated hesperidin and even such inorganic compounds as polymetaphosphate, phosphotungstate, silicotungstate and phosphomyolybdate salts are also active. It is not known whether these agents act to release the same clearing factor containing endogenous heparin, or whether their similar electrostatic capacities allow them to substitute for heparin (57).

It has been argued that endogenous heparin is of physiological importance, because the heparin-binding protamine will not only inhibit clearing factor activity, but will even enhance the turbidity of untreated lipemic plasma. However, toluidine blue, neutral red (basic dyes) and certain heparin-combining alkaloids do not behave in similar fashion. Many other substances inhibit the action of clearing factor, but whether they operate through surface-active properties (e.g. bile salts and detergents) or by the stimulation of a specific clearing factor inhibitor is yet speculative (57).

Whether clearing factor of post-heparin plasma is present physiologically became especially important, in view of the observation that mast cells, known secretors of heparin, are present in decreased numbers in the hearts of patients with advanced atherosclerosis (95). Beyond the lack of specificity of heparin in the activation of serum lipoprotein lipase activity, the suppression of the lipolytic activity by large doses of protamine does not completely prevent the hydrolysis of triglyceride. Nevertheless, many investigators continue to favor the idea that lipoprotein lipase does play a predominant role in fat transport (96). The locale of its action is undoubtedly in the adipose tissue, rather than the blood (89), for only rarely does blood from an untreated subject have clearing factor. In fact, patients with hyperlipemia may not even show the usual development of clearing factor after injection of heparin (96, 97): either they suffer from a tissue deficiency of some sort, or available techniques for isolating their clearing factor from inhibiting factors are inadequate (97). Recent work on "heparin" determinations in the blood suggests that heparin and heparinoids do occur in measurable quantities in normal subjects. It is interesting that the heparin level showed a negative correlation with $S_f^0$0-20 (beta) lipoproteins but none with those of other density (98).

Treatment with Heparin. Obviously, if heparin were continually effective, we should be able to maintain low levels of chylomicra and perhaps low density alpha$_2$ lipoproteins. While it is still not economically feasible to use heparin for long term anticoagulant effect, it is practicable to employ the small doses of heparin required to promote clearing factor once or twice weekly, or even daily. This has not appeared rational inasmuch as the demonstrable effect of heparin upon lipemic clearing is exhausted in four to six hours after intravenous, twenty-four to thirty-six hours after subcutaneous injection. Nevertheless, Engleberg et al. (99) have recently justified such intermittent use of subcutaneously administered heparin (200 mgm. semiweekly) by their practical results in influencing morbidity and mortality rates. The rationale for this therapy is not yet clear and other reports, excepting a few cases who received daily anticoagulant doses from Besterman (100), have indicated that chronic administration of heparin has no permanent effect upon the serum lipids (101).

If an "oral heparin," effective at "clearing" the lipoproteins could be made available, so that injection might be avoided, this would be a safe and perhaps practical treatment regimen. A sublingual form of heparin has been advanced as the answer to this proposal, but so far a discouraging report about the effectiveness of sublingual heparin leaves one undecided as to the ultimate virtue of presently available products (102).

Lipid Mobilizing Factor. Seifter and Baeder (103) showed that the plasma obtained from rats after cortisone administration, exposure to cold, or production of nephrotoxic nephrosis contained a heat stable inhibitor of clearing factor. Dialysis of plasma so derived was capable of concentrating the activity, so that injection of the dialysate into many species, including man, provoked a dramatic hyperlipemia. This material was isolated, crystallized and found to be a peptide. While it had not been possible to recover this factor from adrenalectomized or hypophysectomized animals, the isolated material injected into such animals was still equally capable of provoking hyperlipemia. Finally, a dialysate from a posterior pituitary extract of the hog was found to have potent lipid mobilizing properties. Other pituitary extracts, such as pitocin and pitressin, and extracts of the anterior lobe of pituitary or of skeletal muscle were completely inactive, so apparently adrenocortical stimulation of the pituitary evokes secretion of this agent.

It was at first considered that this was an inhibitor of naturally occurring clearing factor; but the designation was later changed to *lipid mobilizer,* since some doubt arose that clearing factor was necessarily or exclusively involved in its effect. Chronic administration of this material to dogs led to almost complete atrophy of perirenal, omental, mesenteric and spermatic cord fat: no hepatic lipid deposition was observed. Acute administration produced hyperlipemia in fasting but not in post-prandial animals. In humans it was found to be active in fasting subjects who had been on a low fat diet, but not in those fed carbohydrate or used to a high fat diet. It is difficult to see how this might be explained by inhibition of clearing factor, which would presumably be called upon in greater amounts in the latter instance.

Protamine hyperlipemia was originally explained as a neutralization of heparin and hence clearing factor. However, Seifter et al. (103) observed that protamine injection failed to induce hyperlipemia in adrenalectomized or hypophysectomized animals, in contrast to the lipid mobilizer, and contrary to expectations, if it served to inhibit clearing factor. They concluded that protamine produced its hyperlipemia by stimulating the pituitary production of lipid mobilizer. It is hard to reconcile this conclusion with the *in vitro* studies which demonstrate an inhibition of clearing factor in the test tube.

Partially depolymerized hyaluronic acid. This material, like hyaluronidase, hyaluronic acid and desoxycorticosterone, was found to induce clearing factor production; unlike the others it was active orally. It is a non-sulfated polysaccharide akin to heparin, which has been shown to have an anti-hyperlipemic effect in experimental rat nephrosis, human essential hyperlipemia, and animals previously treated with lipid mobilizer (103). The delactescent effect differs from that of clearing factor in that no lipolysis occurs—fatty acids are not released. In the few instances studied, the effect, but not the concentration, of lipid mobilizer seems to be inhibited. According to the work of this same group, lipid mobilizer is secreted in large amounts under the stress of surgery, but its effect is inhibited by this incompletely depolymerized hyaluronic acid even though lipid mobilizer activity could still be found in the portal venous blood (104). Reports on the effectiveness of this or similar agents upon the lipoprotein pattern of essential hyperlipemia, essential hypercholesterolemia and other disease states are awaited with great interest.

"STRESS"

Whether "psychosomatic" factors involving the adrenocortical-pituitary axis or the autonomic nervous system may be important in determining the height of the serum lipid has always been a matter for concern. It is an old clinical impression that myocardial infarction often succeeds unusual emotional or physical strain. A nagging uncertainty that has loomed large to clinicians interested in this area is the possibility that the correlations which exist between certain serum lipids and manifest coronary disease may simply result from a cognate of both. Could the various relationships between coronary atherosclerosis and serum lipids, hypertension, smoking or family history each and all be explained by a common substratum of frustration, chronic anxiety, nervous tension, "increased pace of life," and so forth, which is associated with the more highly developed modern societies. In spite of important correlation between the degree and severity of atherosclerosis found clinically and at autopsy in patients with diabetic, nephrotic and essential idiopathic hypercholesteremia (xanthoma tendinosum) and hyperlipemia (xanthoma tuberosum) (105), this is not an untenable thesis. Several interesting and pertinent observations have been made which do suggest that the lipid levels in the blood, as well as the clotting mechanism, are influenced by emotional factors. Evidence that adrenocortical hormones may mediate this effect is poor (56), but the possibility that the autonomic nervous system and adrenomedullary hormones might be chronically involved has not been seriously studied.

Groen et al. (106) were the first to describe diphasic fluctuations in the serum cholesterol level in subjects of dietary experiments who sustained concern over financial matters, "conflict" with an employer, strenuous physical exertion and intercurrent illness. The authors have also observed such variations in serum cholesterol associated with these things.

Friedman, Rosenman and Carroll (107), in following a group of tax accountants who performed peak overloads of work just prior to income tax deadlines of January 31 and April 15, observed a rise in serum cholesterol and a fall in Lee-White clotting time as these deadlines approached. In a later study, a group of executives were selected by laymen as "alert, driving, ambitious and competitively striving toward self-selected (but poorly-defined) goals." When compared with a control group, judged both by their peers and by psychiatric interview to represent the opposite extreme, they were found to be constantly driving to meet deadlines, to have higher serum cholesterol levels, lower clotting times and a greater incidence of clinical coronary disease. This aggressive group was in still greater contrast to a group of blind men, presumed to have a special type of chronic anxiety (. . . "an air of resignation, worry, and hopelessness"), which involved no deadlines (108). Other authors (109, 110) have observed highly significant increases in the serum cholesterol of students at examination times, when compared with a mid-semester value. Ultracentrifugal lipoprotein analyses showed that the $S_f^o0\text{-}12$ class showed no significant change, whereas a dramatic change occurred in the $S_f^o12\text{-}400$ classes.

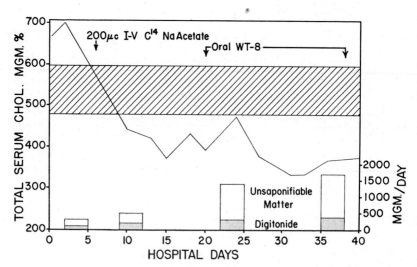

Figure 7. A plot of the serum cholesterol level against days in the hospital for patient B. C. The horizontal shaded area represents the range of her serum cholesterol values in over forty bleedings made during the preceding two year period, exclusive of another hospitalization (for myocardial infarction) when a transitory elevation to 671 mgm.% was seen. The bars below indicate the total unsaponifiable matter (u.m.) and the digitonin precipitable u.m. of the feces expressed as milligrams per day; the two right hand bars indicating 3-day stool collections while on the brain extract (WT-8).

An experience in one of our patients is further argument for the significant effect that fear may have upon the serum cholesterol level: B. C. was a fifty-six year old woman with familial hyper-cholesterolemia and xanthoma tendinosum, previous myocardial infarctions and a residual anginal syndrome. She was invited to enter the hospital for experimental studies on cholesterol metabolism. In Figure 7 is seen the fluctuation in her serum cholesterol level that followed. One sample of blood was drawn in the first week, during which accommodation to the hospital regime was permitted. In conversation with the patient, it was discovered that, in spite of the painstaking explanations as to the purpose of her hospitalization, she had become convinced that it was for the treatment of a dreaded malignancy. This was only confirmed when she found herself admitted to the Argonne Cancer Research Hospital. The sharp rise to 703 mgm.% (this analysis was repeated) could not be explained by any dietary change, for the cholesterol later fell to abnormally low levels, though the dietary fat remained the same, and the patient agreed that this was at the same level she had used at home. Once her cancerphobia was allayed and she became accustomed to the hospital routine, levels subnormal for her developed. The serum cholesterol values reached during the period of a brain extract administration (WT-8) were slightly lower than the values during the control period, which were rising again from the low levels seen in the period of recovery from her unique stress.

There is little doubt that the serum cholesterol can fluctuate dramatically with acute disturbances in the psychosomatic equilibrium. Whether chronic emotional disturbances can lead to chronic elevation of the serum cholesterol level, whether this is related to a particular hormonal stimulation, and what this may have to do with the relationship between blood cholesterol levels and coronary artery disease remains to be established. In any case, we must be cautious in interpreting changes in serum cholesterol as due to a treatment when they might also be attributable to psychic influences secondary to hospitalization, or to other elaborate changes in the subject's pattern of living.

Chapter III

THERAPEUTIC EFFORTS

WHILE PROPER manipulation of the diet is often capable of achieving a reduction of the serum lipids, any doctor who has prescribed a weight reduction diet can attest to the fact that long-term dietary therapy in asymptomatic people is very difficult to maintain, in contrast to the chronic administration of a pill or capsule. Furthermore, there are some cases of stubborn hypercholesteremia which have an inadequate response to dietary fat restriction. Inasmuch as no hormonal agent has yet been shown to lower the serum lipid levels short of undesirable effects, several other therapeutic agents have been studied. These can be divided into agents which interfere with cholesterol absorption, so that it is lost in the feces; those which interfere with cholesterol synthesis; and those which operate by mechanisms not yet understood. It will be seen that, so far, the ideal agent has not been found.

FECAL SEQUESTRATION OF ALIMENTARY CHOLESTEROL

The cholesterol in the alimentary canal is derived from the diet, from the bile which enters the duodenum, and probably from direct secretion by and mucosal sloughing of the intestinal wall. Substantial reabsorption of cholesterol normally occurs in the small intestine, and requires the presence of bile salts and probably some neutral fat. Whether all of the cholesterol absorbed must be esterified as it passes from the intestinal mucosa is not certain, for ten to twenty percent free cholesterol normally appears in the chyle. On the other hand, when fat is removed from the diet, cholesterol absorption is markedly, if not completely, suppressed. In any case, the intestinal mucosal cells play an active part in the process of cholesterol esterification and incorporation into the chylomicra which ultimately appear in the lacteals and travel to the peripheral fat depots or the liver (111) . At one time, it was argued that cholesterol synthesis was sufficiently active so that removal of cholesterol from the diet, or presumably from the entero-hepatic cycle, could not be expected to have much effect on the total cholesterol of the body, or of the blood. It must now be conceded that considerable "slack" must exist in this homeostatic regulation, for several agents have been reported to lower serum cholesterol by presumably interfering with its reabsorption.

Beta-sitosterol. This is a plant sterol (phytosterol) identical to cholesterol in its ring configuration but containing twenty-nine carbons, due to an extra ethyl group in the side chain (see Figure 1). It is almost as ubiquitous in the vegetable kingdom as cholesterol is in the animal kingdom. Many investigators have confirmed the fact that 15 to 20 grams per day of this compound, when administered as an oral emulsion, will reduce serum cholesterol levels substantially in animals (112) and by fifteen to twenty percent in human subjects (113-115). It is apparently quite safe and side effects are not serious; they are, however, uncomfortable enough to many patients so that, when coupled with the substantial expense involved for such an uncertain gain, they do not care to take this preparation for the rest of their lives.

TABLE 2

COMPARISON OF MEAN SERUM CHOLESTEROL LEVELS IN SIX PATIENTS DURING
TREATMENT WITH CYTELLIN AND BRAIN EXTRACT (WT-5)

	Control			Cerebroside (WT-5)			Cytellin		
Patient	Low	Mean	±S.D.	Low	Mean	±S.D.	Low	Mean	±S.D.
C.A.	215	270	±38	207	215	± 9	202	216	±10
R.G.	315	332	±32	276	295	±16	280	293	±12
M.L.	286	312	±16	190	241	±35	241	255	±12
H.K.	223	280	±34	196	215	±10	205	228	±19
S.S.	345	424	±45	326	371	±20	347	389	± 8
M.B.	368	408	±32	284	302	±15	270	285	±18

Brain Extract. The authors have had considerable experience with a decholesterolized extract of brain which is largely a mixture of crude cerebrosides and seems to work in a fashion and extent similar to sitosterol, though by an apparently different mechanism (50). A comparison of the clinical effectiveness of these two agents in influencing cholesterol levels may be seen in Table 2.

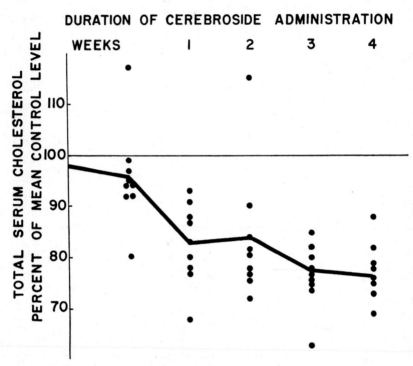

Figure 8. Response of the serum cholesterol to 40 gm./day of a crude cerebro-side fraction of brain. Each dot represents a serum cholesterol determination in each of nine patients, expressed as the percent of a mean control value for that individual. The heavy line represents the average curve of cholesterol reduction (ref. 116).

Figure 8 illustrates the fall in cholesterol obtained by the administration for one month of 40 gm. per day of the powdered crude cerebrosides to nine patients who had hypercholesteremia and coronary artery disease (116). The average lipoprotein levels in these same nine cases are presented in Figure 9. It can be seen that the -$S_{1,21}$ 20-40 (beta) lipoproteins are reduced, the -$S_{1,21}$ 0-10 (alpha$_1$) lipoproteins rise slightly, but not significantly, during the treatment period.

A broad scale clinical trial was accomplished using a sorbitol emulsion of this same powdered extract (50). This had higher patient acceptance and proved to be at least as effective as the bulk powder, but the required daily dose of the emulsion was three to four ounces. This study demonstrated that the magnitude of the serum cholesterol response varied directly with the dosage of material taken (up to 40 gm. per day of the extract) and with the initial height of the cholesterol level. The adherence to a previously prescribed low fat diet did not mitigate the response, nor did a mild degree of weight gain seen in one-third of the fifty patients studied interfere with this response. Figure 10 shows the serum cholesterol response of these same patients in array.

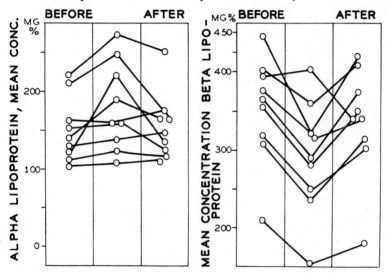

Figure 9. Average lipoprotein values during control (right and left) and treatment (center) periods in the same patients reported in Figure 8; only the alpha$_1$ (-S$_{1.21}$ 0-10) and beta (-S$_{1.21}$ 20-40) lipoproteins are indicated (ref. 116).

Mode of Action. The similarity in the effect of Sitosterol and the brain extract on the serum lipids is not confined to the extent of serum cholesterol reduction. Both lower neutral fat and phospholipid levels of the serum as well as cholesterol. Both must be given in rather large doses, on the order of 20 gm. per day or more, and consequent gastro-intestinal complaints, though mild, are not infrequent. Exacerbation of ulcer symptoms in patients so afflicted, has occurred regularly with the brain extract emulsion, and, in one patient, a bleeding ulcer developed *de novo*. Also, because of the bulk of unabsorbable material given, bowel movements become bulkier and more "regular" with both of these agents.

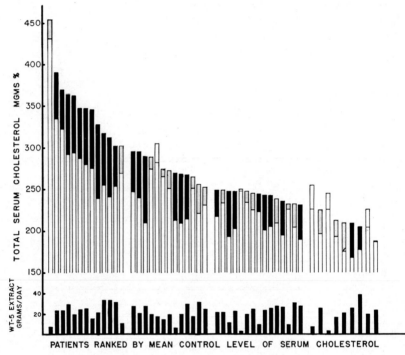

Figure 10. Response of fifty patients to administration of a brain extract emulsion. The average daily dose of the brain extract taken per day is indicated in the lower array. The upper bars indicate averages of total serum cholesterol levels of the individual patients, ranked by their mean level during the control period. The upper shaded portion indicates a fall in mean serum cholesterol with treatment which is statistically significant when black ($P<0.05$), or not significant ($P>0.05$) when gray. Five patients showed a statistically insignificant rise in mean serum cholesterol level, as indicated by the unshaded upper portion (ref. 50).

The mechanism of action of these two agents is apparently different, though both presumably deflect cholesterol from the entero-hepatic cycle into the feces. It has been suggested that sitosterol operates to form unabsorbable mixed crystals with cholesterol (117) or that it competes with cholesterol for cholesterol esterases, either in the intestinal lumen or mucosal cell (118). Tracer studies in rats have indicated, that exogenous C^{14} cholesterol appears in greater amounts in the feces and in reduced amounts in the liver and chyle when soy sterols are administered (119, 120).

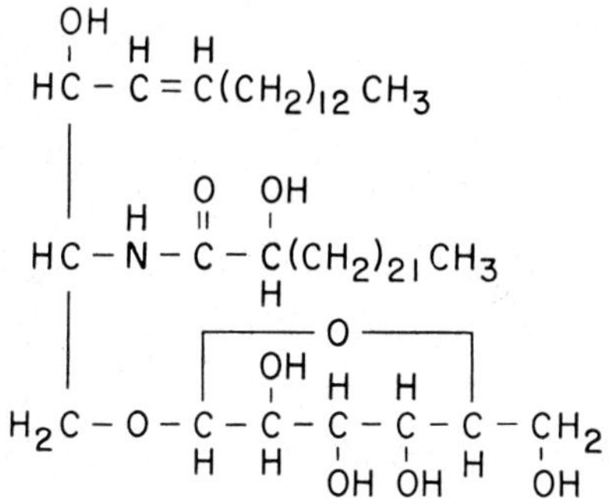

PHRENOSINE 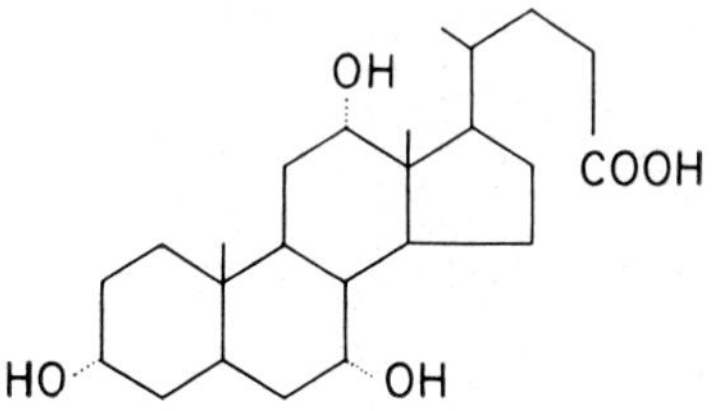   CHOLIC ACID

Figure 11. Left: Phrenosine or cerebron, prototype of the cerebrosides. It is a galactolipid which yields on hydrolysis sphigosine and cerebronic (α-hydroxylignoceric) acid, as well as galactose. The latter is split off most easily to yield the ceramide residue.
Right: Cholic acid (3α, 7α, 12α-trihydroxy cholanic acid) is the most common bile acid of the feces. The other bile acid consistently present in human feces is desoxycholic acid (3α, 12α, dihydroxycholanic acid).

The effectiveness of the brain-cerebroside fraction seems to depend upon its remarkable affinity for cholesterol (36). By our method of fractionation, the cerebroside present in greatest abundance is phrenosine (Figure 11). Purification of the brain extract, which contained about 50% cerebrosides to a 98% pure phrenosine, provided a material which was gram-for-gram no more effective than the original material. Neither crystallographic studies, nor comparisons of esterase activity showed any significant mixed crystal formation or inhibition of esterase activity.*

In two subjects, an increase in fecal sterols, cholesterol and coprostanol, was found during cerebroside administration. In one

---

*For these studies we are indebted to the biophysical laboratories of Eli Lilly and Company.

patient, where fecal bile acid excretion was measured, a parallel increase in desoxycholic and cholic acids was observed. Radioisotope studies in these same subjects suggested that there was no striking increase in conversion of intravenously injected C^{14} acetate into circulating cholesterol, as compared to that during a control period, and the exhibition of the cerebroside fraction induced a more rapid decline in the serum cholesterol specific activity. This may be explained by the strong attraction between the cerebroside residue (the ceramide) and the sterol of the feces. In these studies even ten recrystallizations in ethanol did not remove all cholesterol. In one particular in vitro system, this affinity was further demonstrated by recrystallization of the cerebroside extract dissolved in hot acetone which contained a known amount of cholesterol. This caused a loss from solution of about 2 mgm. of cholesterol per 50 mgm. of cerebroside precipitated (36).

While both of these agents lower the serum cholesterol significantly (about 20 percent), what of the individual lipoproteins? Neither seems to influence the alpha$_1$ lipoprotein level, both affect the beta$_1$ lipoprotein level of the serum (115, 116). The lower density S$_f$20-100 lipoproteins were "not consistently effected" by sitosterol (114). In nine patients treated with the brain extract and fifteen of those treated with the emulsion preparation, there was primarily a fall in the beta lipoprotein ($-S_{1,21}$20-40) with only inconsistent effects on the lighter density material ($-S_{1,21}$ 70-400) (115).

Bile Acid Interference. With the demonstration by Siperstein et al. (121) that bile salts are obligatory to cholesterol absorption, plus the previously established fact that, at least in the rat, bile acids are a catabolic end product of cholesterol metabolism (122, 123), attempts to bind these cholanic acid derivatives (Figure 11) have had great appeal as a hypocholesteremic measure. Siperstein and coworkers (124) showed that the feeding of ferric chloride to cholesterol-fed chicks prevented the usual hypercholesteremic response, presumably because of its ability to bind the bile acids. Recently a preliminary report has indicated that the use of a basic anion exchange resin in patients can lower serum levels by approximately 20%, presumably by this same mechanism (125). Many experimenters have taken to adding cholate salts to the usual rat diet in order to achieve strikingly high levels of serum cholesterol (28, 44, 126).

This approach may yet provide a significant means of influencing serum cholesterol, for with the removal of bile acids from the entero-hepatic cycle cholesterol reabsorption is hindered on the one hand, while the cholesterol pool in the liver and serum is depleted by bile acid replacement on the other. As has been noted, the best explanation to date for the manner in which many, if not all, foodstuffs alter cholesterol metabolism is found in their capacity to influence the fecal excretion of bile acids and other sterols related to cholesterol degradation. Abell et al (127) have demonstrated that the sum of fecal sterols and bile acids varies quantitatively with the cholesterol in the diet of the dog. In addition, the bacterial flora of the intestinal tract and the motility of the fecal stream, perhaps influenced by the fecal bulk, seem to play a role in determining the loss of cholesterol and bile acids to the feces (5, 7). Whether the reduction in serum cholesterol due to bile acid excretion might produce any alteration in lipoproteins beyond the beta lipoprotein (S_f0-12) reduction seen with sitosterol or cerebrosides is not certain, but rats fed cholate show a rise principally in the low density serum lipoprotein (44).

INHIBITION OF CHOLESTEROL SYNTHESIS

Nicotinic Acid. An incidental observation in routine studies of blood chemistry on schizophrenic patients who were being given large doses of niacin for short periods indicated that this B-vitamin did lower the serum cholesterol level. In doses of 1.5 to 6 gm. daily, the plasma cholesterol is reduced on the order of 15 to 20%, and can be so maintained for periods up to three years (128, 129). Flushing of the face, fullness in the head, unpleasant gastrointestinal symptoms, nervousness and urticaria have been reported and occasion the necessity for discontinuing the medication in a "small number of cases." It was claimed that the flushing and fullness in the head subside in a week and that "it did not interfere with therapy in any patient who persisted in taking the drug for one week or longer" (129). Interestingly enough, nicotinic acid amide was quite ineffective.

Tests of liver function in patients maintained for a long time on large doses of niacin have shown slight abnormalities: transient slight retention of bromsulphalein, positive cephalin flocculation tests, and slight elevation of alkaline phosphatase have been observed in occasional patients. Blood glucose levels become elevated in some patients and glucose tolerance decreased in others. Whether these are manifestations of damage or a unique function of administering such large doses of a vitamin important to carbohydrate metabolism is not clear, but they usually subsided on reducing the dose of niacin (130). Recently a case has been reported in which jaundice occurred, presumably due to cholestasis for it cleared on withdrawal of the drug (131). It might also be mentioned that at least two cases of myocardial infarction have occurred in spite of nicotinic acid therapy (128). Thus, nicotinic acid seems to lower cholesterol about as efficiently as sitosterol or even thyroid analogues, but at the large doses necessary, it is not without discomfort and perhaps danger.

The mechanism of action of niacin is not clear. On paper electrophoresis the primary change is in the beta rather than in the $alpha_1$ lipoprotein cholesterol, but ultracentrifugal studies have not been reported. At the same time it is noted that female patients respond more dramatically than males. Goldsmith, et al. (35) showed no changes in the fecal excretion of sterols or bile acids in patients treated with nicotinic acid. Merrill (132) observed an increased synthesis of cholesterol *in vivo* and *in vitro* in rats fed 0.8 percent nicotinic acid; whereas, Duncan and Best (133) reported, in preliminary form, that long term feeding of 1% nicotinic acid to rats induced in depression of the incorporation of acetate into serum and liver cholesterol. This latter work suggests the possibility that a hepatic disability may develop with time and be responsible for the reduced cholesterol levels. It has long been known that liver impairment leads to low levels of serum cholesterol.

After disappointing hepatic and arterial wall deposits had been noted with Δ-4-cholestenone, α-phenylbutyrate and its amide were reported to be potent inhibitors of cholesterol synthesis *in vitro* and *in vivo*, and have received clinical trial. Cottet and coworkers (134) have reported dramatic effects upon serum cholesterol in over 100 subjects, but this has been contradicted (135) . Current preliminary reports suggest that MER-29, *Triparanol®*, ((4-diethylaminoethoxy) phenyl) -1- (P-tolyl) -2 (P-chlorophenyl) ethanol, is a potent inhibitor of cholesterol synthesis in the liver (136) . Animal experiments already indicate that the synthetic pathway of cholesterol is disturbed in an inhibitory way with the production of new abnormal substances (137) : the livers of treated rats accumulated a sterol which behaved like desmosterol (138) . It has been used in some human subjects with significant reduction in serum cholesterol levels (139) , but the total sterol levels are only slightly effected and the hepato-toxicity of a similar agent (benzmalacene) must not be forgotten (140) .

MISCELLANEOUS COMPOUNDS

Portman and Stare (7) have reviewed the suppressive effects upon cholesterol synthesis and lipid levels that have been seen in experimental animals treated with vanadium, iron, cobalt and magnesium. Other trace metals have also been implicated (141) . Of these, magnesium is perhaps the most worthy of clinical investigation. Low magnesium levels are associated with high serum cholesterol levels, whereas high levels of dietary magnesium protect hypercholesteremic rats against sudanophilic arterial lesions. In man, while the degree of protection against atherosclerosis is uncertain, there seems to be no consistent relationship between serum levels of cholesterol and magnesium (142) .

Para-amino-salicylic acid (PAS) has recently been reported to lower serum lipid levels. It was first noted in tuberculous patients receiving large doses of the drug who developed all other signs of myxedema but had a low serum cholesterol level. The effect on serum cholesterol is a 30% reduction; more dramatic than that seen with niacin (143) . Unfortunately, the dosage required is known to produce mild but frequent gastrointestinal irritation, and some risk of hypothyroidism must also be considered if this drug were to be used chronically.

Other antibiotics have also been investigated as to their effect on serum cholesterol levels. *Neomycin,* a potent intestinal antibiotic, is perhaps the most successful agent in this regard even though it is used in doses ordinarily considered too small to effectively sterilize the large intestine. Other antibiotics are apparently ineffective and the mechanism of action of both PAS and neomycin are not yet understood (144).

REVIEW OF THERAPY

The Council on Pharmacy and Chemistry of the American Medical Association, in a discussion of the use of sitosterol in coronary disease, stated: "since conclusive evidence of beneficial effects in the prevention or treatment (of this disease) is lacking, therapeutic trial of sitosterols is justified only on the basis of their apparent safety and the inadequacy of any other current form of therapy" (145). Certainly, in the absence of final proof that significant improvement in morbidity and mortality rates follow the sustained reduction of serum lipid levels, the prime dictum must be: "do no harm." While research will continue to go forward in this area, the patient must not be made overly conscious of his "cholesterol count." Not only should he suffer no physical harm, but his equanimity, his mode of life, his livelihood should not be put in jeopardy. Furthermore, any agent which is to be taken chronically and which will require many years for its evaluation should preferably be free from any side effects which will discourage its long term use. The ultimate benefit of any regimen will be ascertained only by a scrupulously controlled study which is large in scope and long in time to allow for the natural vicissitudes of atherosclerotic disorders.

In the long-term management of the patient with coronary disease, there are certain areas of general agreement. Obesity is undesirable, if only because of actuarial findings. A reduction diet will provide a hemodynamic advantage to the injured heart and effect a reduction in serum lipids, including all the low density lipoproteins. The more consistently and gradually this weight reduction is pursued, the longer we may expect the salutary effects upon the serum lipids to operate. The long-term use of anticoagulant therapy has shown impressive results in reducing subsequent mortality and may prove valuable in any case of established coronary artery disease, except when the risk of its use is too great. Certainly emotional tranquility is a desirable attainment in these cases, and not only because of the effect this may have on blood clotting, the serum lipid level and the height of the blood pressure.

What of the serum lipid levels? How low is "normal?" How high is safe? Which lipid factor is the important one? Will reduction of certain serum lipoproteins protect against thrombosis and preclude the necessity of dicumarol therapy? The answer to the last question is not known. There is some evidence from the Framingham Study (55), however, that the frequency of development of new coronary disease is no lower in men whose serum cholesterol is below 225 mgm.% than in those whose level is between 225 and 275 mgm.%. Thus, it would appear that a serum cholesterol level below 275 mgm.% might be considered "safe," though probably lower levels would be desirable, if any effort to reverse the process of intimal accumulation of lipid is to be made. The evidence presented in the foregoing section suggests that the maintenance of reduced serum levels of low density alpha$_2$ lipoproteins, and probably the chylomicra, might attenuate the process of atherogenesis. Because thrombosis is also influenced by still poorly defined serum lipid factors, the reduction of other lipoprotein levels may also be important, although some other parameter of the blood lipids may better indicate this thrombogenic potential. Of the agents reviewed here, what of their effects upon the individual serum lipoproteins?

The *chylomicra* are most effectively reduced by heparin administration, but the chronic use of this agent presents practical difficulties already pointed out. The partially depolymerized hyaluronic acid preparation gives promise in this direction, if initial studies can be confirmed. Any agent modifying the chylomicra may also effect the low density alpha$_2$ lipoprotein level of the serum.

The *low density alpha$_2$ lipoproteins* are apparently influenced by emotional factors and presumably their level in the serum might be influenced favorably by alleviation of anxiety, perhaps by sedation. Reduction in carbohydrate intake, whether or not accompanied by restriction of calories, will lower the low density alpha$_2$ lipoproteins. The estrogenic hormone, in addition to increasing the alpha$_1$ lipoprotein and decreasing the beta$_1$ lipoprotein, may possibly also lower these lipoproteins of the serum.

Beta lipoproteins are reduced by thyroid hormone and its analogues; sitosterol; brain extract; and dietary reduction of animal fat, whether or not replaced by unsaturated fats or associated with calorie reduction. No specific statement can be made concerning the lipoprotein alterations induced by the other hypocholesteremic agents, but, until proven otherwise, it is safe to presume a predominant effect upon the beta lipoprotein level.

Heavy density alpha$_1$ lipoproteins are influenced by the gonadal hormones, or their analogues, and perhaps increased following heparin administration.

In the present state of our knowledge, normalization of an elevated serum cholesterol would seem desirable, provided there is no risk and minimal discomfort to the patient. It should be appreciated that the regimens which most dramatically reduce the serum cholesterol effect mainly the beta lipoproteins, but that there is no good proof that this may be helpful in reducing morbidity and mortality. In fact, there is a strong suggestion that it is the lipoproteins of still lighter density which are important in plaque formation. Further chemical studies are needed to establish the relative role of the various lipid parameters in the clinical disease, but until this has been accomplished the practising physician is probably justified in guiding his therapeutic efforts by the cholesterol level alone. Although dietary manipulation is safe and, in the majority of coronary disease patients, effective at normalizing the serum lipid pattern; its protracted use demands the disestablishment of culturally promoted food habits of a lifetime. While none of the effective pharmacologic agents so far investigated is, in the authors' opinion, sufficiently safe for general use, there is hope that safe and effective chemical regulation of the serum lipids will yet evolve.

REFERENCES

1. Gofman, J. W., Glazier, F., Tamplin, A., Strisower, B. and De-Lalla, O.: Lipoproteins, Coronary Heart Disease and Atherosclerosis. Physiol. Rev., *34:* 589, 1949.
2. Gofman, J. W. et al.: Evaluation of Serum Lipoprotein and Cholesterol Measurements as Predictors of Clinical Complications of Atherosclerosis. Report of a Cooperative Study of Lipoproteins and Atherosclerosis. Circulation, *14:* 691, 1956.

3. Morrison, L. M.: Reduction of Mortality Rate in Coronary Atherosclerosis by a Low Cholesterol-Low Fat Diet. Am. Hrt. J., *42:* 538, 1951.

4. Lyon, T. P., Yankley, A., Gofman, J. W. and Strisower, B.: Lipoproteins and Diet in Coronary Heart Disease. A Five Year Study. California Med., *84:* 325, 1956.

5. Ahrens, E. H. Jr.: Nutritional Factors and Serum Lipid Levels. Am. J. Med., *23:* 928, 1957.

6. Katz, L. N., Stamler, J. and Pick, R.: *Nutrition and Atherosclerosis.* 1958. Lea and Febiger, Philadelphia.

7. Portman, O. and Stare, F. J.: Dietary Regulation of Serum Cholesterol. Physiol. Rev., *39:* 407, 1959.

8. Gofman, J. W.: *Coronary Heart Disease.* Charles C Thomas, Springfield, Ill., 1959.

9. *Chemistry of Lipids as Related to Atherosclerosis.* Edited by I. H. Page, Charles C Thomas, Springfield, Ill., 1957.

10. Symposium on Atherosclerosis. Publ. #338. National Academy of Science—National Research Council, 1954. Washington 25, D. C.

11. *The Blood Lipids and the Clearing Factor.* 3rd. International Conference on Biochemical Problems of Lipids. July, 1956. Koninklijke Vlaamse Academie voor Weltens happer Letteren, en Schone Kunsten von Belgie. Paleis der Academien. Brussels, 1956.

12. The Influence of Hormones in Lipid Metabolism in Relation to Atherosclerosis. Edited by A. Drury 1959, Ann. New York Acad. Sci. vol. *72,* Art 14, 1959 .

13. *Hormones and Atherosclerosis.* Edited by G. Pincus, 1959. Academic Press Inc., New York.

14. Keys, A., Anderson, J. T. Mikelsen, O., Adelson, S. F. and Fidanze, F.: Diet and Serum Cholesterol in Man. J. Nutr., *59:* 39, 1956.

15. Beveridge, J. M. R., Connell, W. F., Mayer, G. A., and Haust, H. L.: Response of Man to Dietary Cholesterol. Circulation, *20:* 920, 1959.

16. Shull, K. H., Mann, G. V., Andrus, S. B. and Stare, F. J.: Response of Dogs to Cholesterol Feeding. Am. J. Physiol., *176:* 475, 1955.

17. Keys, A. and Anderson, J. T.: The Relationship of the Diet to the Development of Atherosclerosis in Man. Symposium on Atherosclerosis. pg. 181, Ref. #10.

18. Steinberg, D. and Fredrickson, D. S.: Inhibitors of Cholesterol

Biosynthesis and the Problem of Hypercholesterolemia. Ann. N. Y. Acad. Sci., *64:* 579, 1956.

19. Nichols, C. W., Jr., Lindsay, S. and Chaikoff, I. L.: Production of Arteriosclerosis in Birds by the Prolonged Feeding of Dihydro-cholesterol. Proc. Soc. Exp. Biol. and Med., *89:* 609, 1955.
20. Cook, R. P., Kliman, A. and Fieser, L. F.: The Absorption and Metabolism of Cholesterol and its Main Companions in the Rabbit—with Observations on the Atherogenic Nature of the Sterols. Arch. Biochm. S. Biophys., *52:* 439, 1954.
21. Kinsell, L. W., Michaels, G. D., Cochrane, G. C., Partridge, J. W., John, J. J. and Balch, H. E.: Effect of Vegetable Fat on Hyper-cholesteremia and Hyperphospholipemia. Diabetes, *3:* 113, 1954.
22. Beveridge, J. M. R., Connell, W. F., Mayer, G. A., Firstbrook, J. B. and DeWolfe, M. S.: The Effects of Certain Vegetable and Animal Fats on the Plasma Lipids of Humans. J. Nutr., *56:* 311, 1955.
23. Beveridge, J. M. R., Connell, W. F. and Mayer, G. A.: Dietary Factors Affecting the Level of Plasma Cholesterol in Humans. The Role of Fat. Canad. J. Biochem. and Physiol., *34:* 441, 1956.
24. Ahrens, E. H., Jr., Blankenhorn, D. H. and Tsaltas, T. T.: Effect on Human Serum Lipids of Substituting Plant for Animal Fats in Diet. Proc. Soc. Exp. Biol. and Med., *86:* 872, 1954.
25. Ahrens, E. H., Jr., Hirsch, J., Insull, W., Jr., Tsaltas, T. T., Blom-strand, R. and Peterson, M. L.: Dietary Control of Lipids in Relation to Atherosclerosis. J. Am. Med. Assoc., *164:* 1905, 1957.
26. Gofman, J. W.: Diet in the Prevention and Treatment of Myo-cardial Infarction. Am. J. Cardiol., *1:* 271, 1958.
27. Keys, A., Anderson, J. T. and Grande, F.: Serum-Cholesterol Re-sponse to Dietary Fat. Lancet, *1:* 787, 1957. Also see Circulation *19:* 201, 1959.
28. Hegsted, D. M., Gotsis, A. and Stare, F. J.: The Effects of Various Fats upon Experimental Hypercholesteremia in the Rat. J. Nutr., *63:* 377, 1957.
29. Ahrens, E. H., Hirsch, J., Peterson, J. L., Insull, W., Stoffel, W., Farquhar, J. W., Miller, T., and Thomasson, H. J.: The Effect on Human Serum Lipids of a Dietary Fat, Highly Unsaturated but Poor in Essential Fatty Acids. Lancet, *1:* 115, 1959.
30. Ahrens, E. H., Jr., Hirsch, J., Insull, W., Jr., and Peterson, M. L.: Dietary Fats and Human Serum Lipid Levels. pg. 222, Ref. #9.

31. Wilson, J. D. and Siperstein, M. D.: Influence of Long Term Fat Feeding on Excretion of Cholesterol-4-C^{14}-Metabolites. Proc. Soc. Exp. Biol. and Med., *99:* 113, 1958.

32. Byers, S. O. and Friedman, M.: Bile Acid Metabolism, Dietary Fats and Plasma Cholesterol Levels. Proc. Soc. Exper. Biol. and Med., *98:* 523, 1958.

33. Hellman, L. and Rosenfeld, R. S.: Isotopic Studies of Cholesterol Metabolism in Man. Page 157. See Ref. #13.

34. Haust, H. L. and Beveridge, J. M. R.: Effect of Varying Type and Quantity of Dietary Fat on the Fecal Excretion of Bile Acids in Humans Subsisting on Formula Diets. Arch. Biochem. and Biophys., *78:* 367, 1958.

35. Goldsmith, G. A., Hamilton, J. G. and Miller, O. N.: Investigation of Mechanisms by which Unsaturated Fats, Nicotinic Acid and Neomycin Lower Serum Lipid Concentration: Excretion of Sterols and Bile Acids. Tr. Ass. Am. Physicians, *72:* 207, 1959.

36. Jones, R. J., Reiss, O. K., and Golden, M. F.: Influence of a Brain Extract upon Cholesterol Metabolism. *International Symposium on Drugs Affecting Lipid Metabolism.* Elsevier, Amsterdam. In press.

37. Hatch, F. T., Abell, L. L. and Kendall, F. E.: Effects of Restriction of Dietary Fat and Cholesterol upon Serum Lipids and Lipoproteins in Patients with Hypertension. Am. J. Med., *19:* 48, 1955.

38. Yudkin, J.: Diet and Coronary Thrombosis; Hypothesis and Fact. *2:* 155, 1957.

39. Keen, H. and Rose, G. A.: Diet and Arterial Disease in a Population Sample. Brit. Med. J., *1:* 1508, 1958.

40. Portman, O. W., Mann, G. V. and Wysocki, A. P.: Bile Acid Excretion by the Rat: Nutritional Effects. Arch. Biochem., *59:* 224, 1955.

41. Mann, G. V., Andrus, S. B., McNally, A. and Stare, F. J.: Experimental Atherosclerosis in Cebus Monkeys. J. Exper. Med., *98:* 195, 1953.

42. Mann, G. V., Farnsworth, D. L. and Stare, F. J.: An Evaluation of the Influence of DL-Methionine Treatment on the Serum Lipids of Adult Males. New Eng. J. Med., *249:* 1018, 1953.

43. Johnson, D., Jr., Leveille, G. A. and Fisher, H.: Influence of Amino Acid Deficiencies and Protein Level on the Plasma Cholesterol of the Chick. J. Nutrition, *66:* 367, 1958.

44. Filios, L. C., Andrus, S. B., Mann, G. V., and Stare, F. J.: Experimental Production of Gross Atherosclerosis in the Rat. J. Exper. Med., *104:* 539, 1956.

45. Jones, R. J. and Huffman, S.: Chronic Effect of Dietary Protein on Hypercholesteremia in the Rat. Proc. Soc. Exper. Biol. and Med., *93:* 519, 1956.

46. Filios, L. C., Naiko, C., Andrus, S. B., Portman, O. W. and Martin, R. S.: Variations in Cardiovascular Sudanophilia with Changes in the Dietary Level of Protein. Am. J. Physiol., *194:* 275, 1958.

47. Nishida, T., Takenaka, F. and Kummerow, F. A.: Effect of Dietary Protein and Heated Fat on Serum Cholesterol and Beta Lipoprotein Levels, and on the Incidence of Experimental Atherosclerosis in Chicks. Circ. Res., *6:* 196, 1958.

48. Stamler, J., Pick, R. and Katz, L. N.: Effects of Dietary Protein and Carbohydrate Level on Cholesterolemia and Atherogenesis in Cockerels on a High-Fat, High-Cholesterol Mash. Circ. Res., *6:* 447, 1958.

49. Keys, A. and Anderson, J. T.: Dietary Protein and the Serum Cholesterol Level in Man. Am. J. Clin. Nutrition., *5:* 29, 1957.

50. Jones, R. J. and Keough, T. F.: Factors in the Hypocholesteremic Response of Patients Given a Brain Extract. J. Lab. and Clin. Med., *52:* 667, 1958.

51. Anderson, J. T., Lawler, A. and Keys, A.: Weight Gain from Simple Overeating. II. Serum Lipids and Blood Volume. J. Clin. Invest., *36:* 81, 1957.

52. Walker, W. J., Lawry, E. Y., Love, D. E., Mann, G. V., Levine, S. A. and Stare, F. J.: Effect of Weight Reduction and Caloric Balance on Serum Lipoprotein and Cholesterol Levels. Am. J. Med., *14:* 654, 1953.

53. Mann, G. V., Teel, K., Hayes, O., McNally, A. and Bruno, D.: Exercise in the Disposition of Dietary Calories. New Eng. J. Med., *253:* 349, 1955.

54. Walker, W. J., Weiner, N. and Milch, L. J.: Differential Effect of Dietary Fat and Weight Reduction in Serum Levels of Beta-Lipoproteins. Circulation, *15:* 31, 1957.

55. Dawber, T. R., Moore, F. E. and Mann, G. V.: Coronary Heart Disease in the Framingham Study. Am. J. Pub. Health, Suppl. to vol. *47,* part 2, page 4, 1957.

56. Adlersberg, D.: Hormonal Influences on the Serum Lipids. Am. J. Med., *23:* 769, 1957.

57. Levy, S. W.: Heparin and the Blood Lipids. Revue Canadienne de Biologie, *17:* 1, 1958.
58. Eilert, M. L.: The Effect of Estrogens on the Partition of the Serum Lipids in Female Patients. Metabolism, *2:* 137, 1953.
59. Russ, E. M., Eder, H. A., and Barr, D. P.: Protein-Lipid Relationships in Human Plasma; in Normal Individuals. Am. J. Med., *11:* 468, 1951.
60. Oliver, M. F. and Boyd, G. S.: Endocrine Aspects of Coronary Sclerosis. Lancet, *2:* 1273, 1956.
61. Chaikoff, I. L., Lindsay, S., Lorenz, F. W. and Entenman, C.: Production of Atheromatosis in the Aorta of the Bird by the Administration of Diethylstilbesterol. J. Exper. Med., *88:* 373, 1948.
62. Pick, R., Stamler, J., Rodbard, S. and Katz, L. N.: The Inhibition of Coronary Atherosclerosis by Estrogens in Cholesterol-Fed Chicks. Circulation, *6:* 276, 1952.
63. Katz, L. N., Stamler, J. and Pick, R.: The Role of the Hormones in Atherosclerosis. page 236, Ref. #13.
64. Stamler, J., Pick, R. and Katz, L. N.: Prevention of Coronary Atherosclerosis by Estrogen-Androgen Administration in the Cholesterol-Fed Chick. Circ. Res., *1:* 94, 1953.
65. Eder, H. A.: The Effects of Sex Hormones on Serum Lipids and Lipoproteins. pg. 335, Ref. #13.
66. Stamler, J., Pick, R., Katz, L. N., Pick, A. and Kaplan, B. M.: Interim Report on Clinical Experiences with Long-Term Estrogen Administration to Middle-Aged Men with Coronary Heart Disease. pg. 423. Ref. #13.
67. Wuest, J. H., Jr., Dry, T. J. and Edwards, J. E.: The Degree of Coronary Atherosclerosis in Bilaterally Ovariectomized Women. Circulation, *7:* 801, 1953.
68. Blumgart, H. L., Freedberg, A. S. and Kurland, G. S.: Hypercholesteremia, Myxedema and Atherosclerosis. Am. J. Med., *14:* 665, 1953.
69. Jones, R. J., Cohen, L. and Corbus, H.: The Serum Lipid Pattern in Hyperthyroidism, Hypothyroidism, and Coronary Atherosclerosis. page 980, Ref. #12.
70. Sholz, W.: *Klinische und Anatomische Untersuchungen über den Cretinismus.* O. Hirschwell. 1906. Berlin, Germany.
71. Report of a Committee of the Clinical Society of London, Chaired by Sir William Ord. Trans. Clin. Soc. London. Suppl. to vol. *21:* Longman's Green, 1888 London, England.

72. Page, I. H. and Brown, H. B.: Induced Hypercholesterolemia and Atherogenesis. Circulation, *6:* 681, 1952.

73. Jones, R. J., Cohen, L. and Corbus, H.: The Serum Lipid Pattern in Hyperthyroidism, Hypothyroidism, and Coronary Atherosclerosis. Am. J. Med., *19:* 71, 1955.

74. Mason, R. L., Hunt, H. M. and Hurxthal, L.: Blood Cholesterol Values in Hyperthyroidism and Hypothyroidism—Their Significance. New England J. Med., *203:* 1273, 1930.

75. Peters, J. P. and Man, E. B.: The Interrelations of Serum Lipids in Patients with Thyroid Disease. J. Clin. Invest., *22:* 715, 1943.

76. Rosenman, R. H., Friedman, M. and Byers, S. O.: Observations Concerning the Metabolism of Cholesterol in the Hypo- and Hyperthyroid Rat. Circulation *5:* 589, 657, 1952. Also: J. Clin. Endocrinol and Metab., *12:* 1287, 1952.

77. Erikson, S.: Influence of Thyroid Activity on Excretion of Bile Acids and Cholesterol in the Rat. Proc. Soc. Exper. Biol. and Med., *94:* 582, 1957.

78. Gould, R. G.: The Relationship between Thyroid Hormones and Cholesterol Biosynthesis and Turnover, pg. 75, Ref. #13.

79. Strisower, B., Gofman, J. W., Galioni, E. F., Almada, A. A., and Simon, A.: Effect of Thyroid Extract on Serum Lipoproteins and Serum Cholesterol. Metabolism, *3:* 218, 1954.

80. Strisower, E. H.: Effect of Desiccated Thyroid Substance and Thyroid Congeners Upon Serum Lipoproteins and Serum Cholesterol Levels. pg. 315, Ref. #13.

81. Strisower, B., Elmhinger, P., Gofman, J. W. and DeLalla, O.: The Effect of L-Thyroxine in Serum Lipoprotein and Cholesterol Concentrations. J. Clin. Endocrinol. and Metab., *:19* 117, 1959.

82. Oliver, M. F. and Boyd, G. S.: The Influence of Tri-iodothyroacetic Acid on the Circulating Lipids and Lipoproteins in Euthyroid Men with Coronary Disease. Lancet, *1:* 124, 1957.

83. Rawson, R. W., Money, W. L., Kroc, R. L., Kumaoka, S., Benua, R. S. and Leeper, R. D.: A Dissociation of Thyroid Hormonal Effects by Structural Alterations of the Thyroxine Molecule. Tr. Ass. Am. Phys., *72:* 225, 1959.

84. Starr, P., Roen, P., Freibrun, J. L. and Schleissner: Reduction of Serum Cholesterol by Sodium Dextro-Thyroxine. A.M.A. Arch. Int. Med. *105:* 830, 1960.

85. Jones, R. J.: Serum Cholesterol Reduction with D-thyroxine. Circulation, *20:* 979, 1959.

86. Pitt-Rivers, R. and Lerman, J.: The Physiological Activity of the Optically Active Isomers of Thyroxine. J. Endocrinol., *5:* 223, 1948.
87. Tapley, D. F., Davidoff, F. F., Hatfield, W. B. and Ross, J. E.: Physiological Disposition of D- and L-Thyroxine in the Rat. Am. J. Physiol., *197:* 1021, 1959.
88. Hahn, R. F.: Abolishment of Alimentary Lipemia Following Injection of Heparin. Science, *98:* 19, 1943.
89. Korn, E. C. and Quigley, T. W.: On the Nature of Lipoprotein Lipase. pg. 255. Ref. 11.
90. Korn, E. C.: Clearing Factor, a Heparin-Activated Lipoprotein Lipase. I Isolation and Characterization of the Enzyme From Normal Rat Heart. J. Biol. Chem., *215:* 1, 1955.
91. Anfinsen, C. B., Boyle, E. and Brown, R. K.: The Role of Heparin in Lipoprotein Metabolism. Science, *115:* 583, 1952.
92. Lindgren, F. T., Freeman, N. K., Nichols, A. V. and Gofman, J. W.: The Physical Chemistry of Lipoprotein Transformation. pg. 224, Ref. 11.
93. Fasali, A., Salteri, F., Spina, G. and Ratti, G.: Ultracentrifugal, Electrophoretic and Chemical Changes Produced in Serum and Artificial Lipid Emulsions by Human "Clearing Factor." pg. 278, Ref. 11.
94. Herbst, F. S. M., Lever, W. F., Lyons, M. E. and Hurley, N. A.: Effects of Heparin on the Lipoproteins in Hyperlipemia. An Electrophoretic Study of the Serum Alpha and Beta Lipoproteins After Their Separation by Fractionation of the Plasma Proteins or Ultracentrifugal Flotation. J. Clin. Invest., *34:* 581, 1955.
95. Cairns, A. and Constantinides, P.: Mast Cells in Human Atherosclerosis. Science, *120:* 31, 1954.
96. Havel, R. J.: Evidence for the Participation of Lipoprotein Lipase in the Transport of Chylomicrons. pg. 265. Ref. 11.
97. Anfinsen, C. B.: Biochemical Aspects of Atherosclerosis. Fed. Proc., *15:* 894, 1956.
98. Yasugi, T., Gofman. J. W., DeLalla, O., Tamplin, A. R., Oshima, K.: Relationship of Blood Heparin Levels to Serum Lipoproteins and Cholesterol Levels in Fasting Subjects. Proc. Soc. Exper. Biol. and Med., *98:* 46, 1958.
99. Engelberg, H., Kuhn, R. and Steinman, M.: A Controlled Study of the Effect of Intermittent Heparin Therapy on the Course of Human Coronary Atherosclerosis. Circulation, *13:* 489, 1956.

100. Besterman, E. M. M.: The Effects of Acute Cardiac Infarction and of Heparin Therapy on the Lipoproteins. Brit. Hrt. J., *20:* 21, 1958.

101. Chandler, H. L. and Mann, G. V.: Heparin Treatment of Patients with Angina Pectoris; Failure to Influence either the Clinical Course or the Serum Lipids. New England J. Med., *249:* 1045, 1953.

102. Engelberg, H.: Buccal and Sublingual Administration of Heparin Potassium (Clarin). J. A. M. A., *169:* p. 1322, 1959.

103. Seifter, J., Baeder, D. H., Zarafonetis, C. J. D. and Kalas, J.: Hormonal Control of Permeability and Mobilization of Fat Depots. page 1031, Ref. #12.

104. Zarafonetis, C. J. D., Seifter, J., Baeder, D., Kalas, J. and Chang, W. Y. M.: Inhibition of Lipid Mobilization of Surgical Stress by Partially Depolymerized Hyaluronic Acid. Am. J. Med. Sci., *237:* 771, 1959.

105. Aldersberg, D. and Schaefer, L. E.: The Interplay of Heredity and Environment in the Regulation of Circulating Lipids and in Atherogenesis (Ed.) Am. J. Med., *26:* 1, 1959.

106. Groen, J., Tjiong, B. K., Kamminga. Chr. E. and Willebrands, A. F.: The Influence of Nutrition, Individuality and Some Other Factors, Including Various Forms of Stress, on the Serum Cholesterol: An Experiment of Nine Months Duration in 60 Normal Human Volunteers. Voeding, *13:* 556, 1952.

107. Friedman, M., Rosenman, R. H. and Carroll, V.: Changes in the Serum Cholesterol and Blood Clotting Time in Man Subjected to Cyclic Variation of Occupational Stress. Circulation, *17:* 852, 1958.

108. Friedman, M. and Rosenman, R. H.: Association of Specific Behavior Pattern with Blood and Cardiovascular Findings. J. A. M. A., *169:* 1286, 1959.

109. Grundy, S. M. and Griffin, A. C.: Effects of Periodic Mental Stress on Serum Cholesterol Levels. Circulation, *19:* 496, 1959.

110. Grundy, S. M. and Griffin, A. C.: Relationship of Periodic Mental Stress to Serum Lipoprotein and Cholesterol Levels. J. A. M. A., *171:* 1794, 1959.

111. Swell, L., Trout, E. C., Jr., Hopper, R., Field, H., Jr., and Treadwell, C. R.: The Mechanism of Cholesterol Absorption. Ann. N. Y. Acad. Sci., *72:* 813, 1959.

112. Peterson, D. W.: Effect of Soybean Sterols in the Diet on Plasma

and Liver Cholesterol in Chicks. Proc. Soc. Exper. Biol. and Med., *78:* 143, 1951.

113. Best, M. M., Duncan, C. H., Van Coon, E. J. and Wathen, J. D.: Lowering of Serum Cholesterol by the Administration of a Plant Sterol. Circulation, *10:* 201, 1954.

114. Best, M. M. and Duncan, C. H.: Modification of Abnormal Serum Lipid Patterns in Atherosclerosis by Administration of Sitosterol. Ann. Int. Med., *45:* 614, 1956.

115. Farquhar, J. W. and Sokolow, M.: Response of Serum Lipids and Lipoproteins of Man to Beta-Sitosterol and Safflower oil. Circulation, *17:* 890, 1958.

116. Jones, R. J.: Serum Cholesterol Reduction in Patients by the Oral Administration of a Brain Extract. J. Lab. and Clin. Med., *47:* 261, 1956.

117. Davis, W. W.: The Physical Chemistry of Cholesterol and Beta-Sitosterol Related to the Intestinal Absorption of Cholesterol. Tr. New York Acad. Sci. (Ser. II), *18:* 123, 1955.

118. Hernandez, H. H., Peterson, D. W., Chaikoff, I. L. and Dauben, W. G.: Absorption of Cholesterol-4-C[14] in Rats Fed Mixed Soybean Sterols and Beta Sitosterol. Proc. Soc. Exper. Biol. and Med., *83:* 498, 1953.

119. Burke, K. A., McCandless, R. F. J. and Kritchevsky, D.: Effect of Soybean Sterols on Liver Deposition of Cholesterol C[-14]. Proc. Soc. Exper. Biol. and Med., *87:* 87, 1954.

120. Hernandez, H. H. and Chaikoff, I. L.: Do Soy Sterols Interfere with Absorption of Cholesterol? *idem.,* *87:* 541, 1954.

121. Siperstein, M. D., Chaikoff, I. L. and Reinhardt, W. O.: C[-14] Cholesterol. V. Obligatory Function of Bile in Intestinal Absorption of Cholesterol. J. Biol. Chem., *198:* 111, 1952.

122. Siperstein, M. D. and Chaikoff, I. L.: C[-14] Cholesterol. III Excretions of Carbons 4 and 26 in Feces, Urine and Bile. J. Biol. Chem., *198:* 93, 1952.

123. Siperstein, M. D. and Chaikoff, I. L.: Conversion of Cholesterol to Bile Acids. Fed. Proc., *14:* 767, 1955.

124. Siperstein, M. D., Nichols, C. W., Jr. and Chaikoff, I. L.: Effects of Ferric Chloride and Bile on Plasma Cholesterol and Atherosclerosis in the Cholesterol-Fed Bird. Science, *117:* 386, 1953.

125. Bergen, S. S., Jr., Van Itallie, T. B., Tennent, D. M. and Sebrell, W. H.: Effect of an Anion Exchange Resin on Serum Cholesterol in Man. Circulation, *20:* 981, 1959.

126. Hegsted, D. M., Andrus, S. B., Gotsis, A. and Portman, O. W.: The Quantitative Effects of Cholesterol, Cholic Acid, and Types of Fat in Serum Cholesterol and Vascular Sudanophilia in the Rat. J. Nutr., *63:* 273, 1957.

127. Abell, L. L., Mosbach, E. H. and Kendall, F. E.: Cholesterol Metabolism in the Dog. J. Biol. Chem., *220:* 527, 1956.

128. Parsons, W. B., Jr., Achor, R. W. P., Berge, K. G., McKenzie, B. F. and Barker, N. W.: Changes in Concentration of Blood Lipids Following Prolonged Administration of Large Dose of Nicotinic Acid to Persons with Hypercholesteremia. Proc. Staff Meeting of Mayo Clinic., *31:* 377, 1956.

129. Parsons, W. B., Jr. and Flinn, J. H.: Reduction of Serum Cholesterol Levels and Beta-Lipoprotein Cholesterol Levels by Nicotinic Acid. A.M.A. Arch. Int. Med., *103:* 783, 1959.

130. Barker, N. W.: The Effect of Niacin on the Blood Cholesterol. Ill. State Med. J., *116:* 1959.

131. Rivin, A. U.: Jaundice Occurring During Nicotinic Acid Therapy for Hypercholesteremia. J. A. M. A., *170:* 2088, 1959.

132. Merrill, J. M.: Effect of Nicotinic Acid on the Incorporation of Radiocarbon into Cholesterol. Circ. Res., *6:* 482, 1958.

133. Duncan, C. H. and Best, M. M.: Effect of Nicotinic Acid on Cholesterol Metabolism of the Rat. Circulation, *18:* 490, 1958.

134. Cottet, J., Mathivat, A. and Redel, J.: Etude Therapeutique d'un Hypocholestérolémiant de Synthèse: L'acid Phényl-ethyl Acétique. Presse Med., *62:* 939, 1955.

135. Oliver, M. F. and Boyd, G. S.: Effect of Phenylethylacetic Acid and Its Amide (Hyposterol) on the Circulating Lipids and Lipoproteins in Man. Lancet, *2:* 829, 1957.

136. Gould, R. G., Lilly, E. H. and Mitchell, V. E.: Effects of MER-29 on Tissue and Plasma Cholesterol Concentrations, and on Hepatic Cholesterol Synthesis from Mevalonic Acid. Circulation, *20:* 965, 1959.

137. Mobberley, M. L., and Frantz, I., Jr.: Observations Concerning the Site of Inhibition of Cholesterol Synthesis by MER-29. Circulation, *20:* 965, 1959.

138. Blohm, T. R. and MacKenzie, R. D.: Specific Inhibition of Cholesterol Biosynthesis by a Synthetic Compound (MER-29). Arch. Biochem. and Biophys., *85:* 245, 1959.

139. Hollander, W. and Chobanian, A.: The Effects of an Inhibitor of Cholesterol Biosynthesis, MER-29, in Subjects with and

without Coronary Artery Disease. Boston Med. Quart., *10:* 37, 1959.

140. Page, I. H. and Schnekloth, R. E.: Hypocholesteremic Effect of Benzmalacene. Circulation, *20:* 1075, 1959.

141. Schroeder, H. A.: Trace Metals in Chronic Disease in *Advances in Internal Medicine., 8:* 259, 1956.

142. Hellerstein, E. E.: Dietary Magnesium and Experimental Atherosclerosis. Ill. State Med. J., *117:* 200, 1960.

143. Tygstrup, N., Winkler, K. and Warburg, E.: Effect of p-Aminosalicylic Acid on Serum Cholesterol. Lancet, *1:* 503, 1959.

144. Samuel, P.: Effect of Neomycin, Para-amino Salicylic Acid and other Antibacterial Drugs on Serum Cholesterol Level of Man. Proc. Soc. Exp. Biol. and Med., *102:* 194, 1959.

145. A.M.A. Council on Pharmacy and Chemistry: Sitosterols. J. A. M. A., *160:* 671, 1956.

INDEX

A

Acetazoleamide, 23-25
Acetyl Digitoxin, 16
Acetyl-K-Strophanthidin, 18
Acid-Base Balance, 23, 31
Actomyosin, 19-20
Adenosinetriphosphate,
  bishydroxycoumarin effect on, 62
  congestive heart failure and, 19
Adipose tissue,
  clearing factor and, 160
Aldosterone, antagonists of, 23, 29
Aglycone, 9, 10
Albumin, role in,
  digitalis binding, 13
  fatty acid metabolism, 160
Alpha₂ globulin,
  antiplasmin activity of, 73
  heparin activation by, 160, 161
  lipoprotein carrier, as, 114, 119
Alpha-phenylbutyrate, 176
Amino acids
  dietary imbalance of, 147
  of lipoproteins, 117
Aminoisometradine, 23
Analytical ultracentrifuge, 113
Aneurysm, aortic, 102
Anion exchange resin, 174
Anticoagulant therapy, 41, 65, 69
  acute myocardial infarct; on, in, 76
  long-term anticoagulant therapy, 77-82
Anticoagulants, oral, 59-65, 76-83
  benefits of, 76, 78-81
  capillary defect from, 64
  chemical formulae of, 60
  clinical comparisons of, 65
  coumarin type, 59-65
  hemorrhage from, 64, 82
  history of, 59
  indanedione drivatives of, 60-62
  metabolism of, 61-63
  molecular structure of, 61

toxicity of, 65
Anti-hemophilic factor, see Factor VIII
Antiheparins, 68
Antiplasmins, 72
Antithrombin effect of heparin, 67
Anxiety and serum lipids, 150, 165
Arachidonic acid, 142
Arterial rupture, aortic, 102
Arterial thrombosis, 42, 43
  atherosclerosis and, 44, 54, 103
Arteriolosclerosis, 101
Arteriosclerosis, 101
Atheromatous plaque, see Atherosclerotic plaque
Atherosclerosis, 54, 101-111
  anxiety and, 165-167
  collagenous degeneration and, 107
  coronary occlusion and, 102-104
  dietary magnesium and, 177
  experimental, 54, 101, 104, 153, 154
  hypercholesteremia and, 165
  hypothyroidism and, 154
  lipids of blood, and,
    see lipids of serum
  ovariectomy and, 154
  pathogenesis, theories of, 104-108,128
  thrombosis and mortality with, 104
  thrombosis, relationship to, 44, 54
Atherosclerotic plaque,
  calcification of, 108
  chemistry of, 108-111
  complications of, 102-104
  formation of, 101-108
  lipid synthesis in, 112
  lipophages in, 101
  lipoproteins of, 125
  phospholipids of, 108, 110, 124
  red cell lipid and, 106, 108, 121, 128
  thrombosis and, 44, 103

B

Bishydroxycoumarin, 58, 61-64
Benzmalacene toxicity, 177

193

Bile acid excretion,
 anion exchange resin effect on, 174
 brain extract and, 174
 dietary carbohydrate and, 147
 dietary fat and, 143-145
 dietary protein and, 150
 thyroid effect on, 156
Bile acid metabolism, 168, 175
Blood coagulation, 46-58. *See also* Fibrin
 formation
Blood hypercoagulability,
 thrombosis and, 42, 44
Blood lipids, *see* Lipids of serum
Blood stasis and thrombosis, 42, 43
Brain extract, 166, 169-174

C

Calcium in atherosclerotic plaque, 101
Calcium, serum level of,
 digitalis toxicity and, 32
 fibrin formation and, 51
 thromboplastin generation and, 49
Carbonic anhydrase inhibition, 6, 23-25
 metabolic acidosis induced by, 24
 renal tubular effect of, 25
 respiratory acidosis, effect on, 25
Cardenolides, 10
Carotenoids,
 atherosclerotic plaque, in the, 111
 lipoprotein constituent, as, 112
Cation exchange resins, 23
Cephalin in,
 arterial wall, 123
 platelets, 49
 thromboplastin, 53
Cerebrosides, 169-174
Ceroid in the,
 atherosclerotic plaque, 111
Chlorothiazide, 6, 23, 25
 acetazoleamide compared with, 26
 blood urea nitrogen elevation by, 28
 electrolyte depletion from, 26
 hepatic coma, and, 28
 hypotensive effect, 28
 mercurial injection, with, 26
Cholestanol, *see* Dihydrocholesterol
Cholestenone, 139
 cholesterol synthesis, inhibition of,
  140, 176

Cholesterol, 138, 139
Cholesterol, ester:free ratio in the,
 atherosclerotic plaque, 108, 121
 lipoproteins, 112, 119, 121
 red cell, 121
 whole serum, 121
Cholesterol, fecal, 143, 144-145, 156, 168,
 172-175
Cholesterol metabolism, 175
 bile salts and, 168
Cholesterol:phospholipid ratio in the,
 atheromatous plaque, 108-110, 122-124
 lipoprotein fractions, 119
 serum, estrogen influence on, 152
Cholesterol, serum level of. *See also*
  Lipids of serum
 antibiotics and, 177
 anxiety, effect of, 150, 165
 benefit from reduction of, 137
 bile acid interference with, 174
 clinical significance, 137, 179
 dietary cholesterol effects on, 138
 dietary fat and, 142-145
 dietary magnesium and, 177
 dietary protein and, 147
 estrogenic effect on, 152
 fecal end products of, 143-145
 intestinal flora and, 147
 obesity and, 151
 thyroxine analogues and, 157-159
Cholesterol, synthesis of,
 inhibition of, 175-177
 thyroid effects on, 156
Christmas factor, *see* Factor IX
Chylomicra and blood clotting, 54
Clearing factor, 159-163
Clotting time
 anxiety and, 166
 heparin, and, 69
 tests of, 50
Coagulation factors, 46-53
  and see individual factors
 bishydroxycoumarin and, 61
 heparin and, 67
 Quick's prothrombin test and, 58
 plasmin inactivation of, 72
Complement
 heparin effect on, 67
 plasmin inactivation of, 72

Congestive heart failure, 5
  adenosine triphosphate, and, 19
  cause of death, as, 77
  dietary sodium in, 6
  digitalization for, 7, 14, 16, 17
  serum electrolytes and therapy of, 31-33
  therapy of, 6, 7, 21-23, 33
Convallotoxin, 9
Cooperative study of lipoproteins and atherosclerosis, 125-127
Coprostanol (coprosterol) , 11, 12, 143
Corn oil, 141
Coronary artery disease, 76, 102-104
  anxiety and, 166
  collateral coronary circulation and, 43
  estrogen, long-term therapy with, 153
  heparin treatment and, 162
  pathology vs. symptoms of, 103
  phospholipids, serum levels of, 53
  prediction of, 125
  thyroactive compounds and, 157
Coronary artery occlusion,
  role of the plaque in, 103
  thrombosis in, 42, 44, 103
Cottonseed oil, 141
Coumarin, derivatives of, 60-63
Cystic medial necrosis, 102

D

Death rate, *see* Mortality rate
7-Dehydrocholesterol, 139
Desmosterol from triparanol, 177
Diet
  blood clotting time, effect of fat in, 54
  carbohydrate in
    fibrinolysin, effect on, 74
    lipoproteins effected by, 146
    plasma free fatty acids and, 54
  cholesterol in, 138
  cholesterol absorption and, 168
  fat in, 140-145
  fibrinolysis and, 74
  protein in, 147-148
  rice diet, 140, 146
  sodium restricted, 6
  sterols in, 138
  weight reduction, 150, 178

Dicumarol®, *see* Bishydroxycoumarin
Digilanid®, 16
Digitalis
  actomysin and, 20
  bufadienolides, 9
  cardenolides, 9
  cedilanid-D, 17
  chemical structure
    desoxyhexoses, 9
    hydroxyl groups, 14
    lactone ring, 9, 10, 13
    stereoconfiguration, 11, 12
  clinical effects, 15-18
  contractile protein, effect on, 19
  deacetyl digitanids, *see* Lanatosides
  D. Lanata, 7, 8
  D. Purpurea, 7
  digitalinum verum, 10
  digitoxin, 9, 10, 15, 16, 19
  digoxin, 10, 17
  gitoxin, 9, 10
  glucoverodoxine, 10
  glycosides, cardioactive, 7-19
  glycosides, polarity of, 13
  lanatosides, 8, 14, 17
  mechanism of action, 19
  metabolism of, 18
  potassium, effects on, 19, 20, 32
  sources of, 7
  strospeside, 10
  therapy, 7, 14, 16, 17
  toxic effects of, 15-18, 32
Digitoxigenin, 10, 12
Digoxigenin, 10, 11
Digoxin, 10, 17
Dihydrochlorothiazide, 28
Dihydrocholesterol, 11, 12, 139
  atheromatosis due to, 140
Diuretics, 6, 21-29
  digitalis toxicity, induced by, 32

E

Edema formation,
  aldosterone in, 29
  congestive heart failure and, 5
Electrolytes of serum, disturbance of
  acetazolamide, 24
  chlorothiazide, 26

congestive heart failure, and therapy of, 31-33
Encrustation theory of atherogenesis, 106
Endothelial injury
  atherogenesis and, 106
  thrombosis and, 42, 44, 55, 74
Endothelial fibrosis, local, 101
Essential fatty acids, 110, 142
Estrogens, serum lipid effects of, 152-154
Ethoxyzolamide, 22, 25
Ethylbiscoumacetate, 63
Ethylenediamine tetra-acetate in digitalis toxicity, 33
Exercise
  fibrinolysin, effect on, 74
  serum lipids, effect on, 150

F

Factor V, 47-50, 53
  deficiency of, 56
  dicumarol effect on, 62
  heparin effect on, 67
  in hemostasis, 55
Factor VII, 47, 49, 50, 53
  deficiency of, 56
  dicumarol effect on, 62
  in hemostasis, 56
Factor VIII, 47-50, 53
  heparin effect on, 67
Factor IX, 47-50, 53
  dicumarol effect on, 62
Fatty acids, bound
  atherosclerotic plaque, in the, 110
  dietary effects of, 140-143
  thromboplastic activity in phospholipids and, 49
Fatty acids, free
  blood coagulation and, 52
  chain length and coagulation, 53
  chain length and dietary effect, 143
  heparin induced, 160
Ferric chloride, feeding of, 174
Fibrin
  clot in atherogenesis, 106
  clot, structure of, 52
  fibrinogen conversion to, 46, 51
  formation and hemostasis, 55, 56
  physiological, 52

plasmin inactivation of, 72
plasminogen affinity for, 71
polymerization of, 51, 52
serum lipids and formation of, 52
thrombin, affinity for, 56
Fibrinogen
  conversion to fibrin, 46, 51
  plasminogen contaminant, 70
Fibrinolysin, 70. *See also* Plasmin
  inhibition in thrombosis, 43
Fibrinolysis, 52, 70, 73-75
Fibrin-stabilizing-factor, 52
Flumethiazide, 29

G

Galactoside in atherosclerotic plaque, 108
Gitalin, 8, 17
Gitaloxin, 10, 11, 17
Gitorin, 10
Gitoxin, 10, 11
Glucoverodoxine, 10
Glycerol, heparin release of, 160

H

Hageman factor, 47-50, 62
  deficiency of, 55
Hellebrin, 9
Hemophilia, 55, 56
Hemorrhage,
  anticoagulants, and, 64, 69, 82
  atherosclerotic plaque, into the, 103-105, 107
  heparin, induced by, 69
  theory of atherogenesis, 107
Hemosiderin in the atherosclerotic plaque, 110
Hemostasis, 41, 55-58
Hemostatic balance, 73
Heparin, 65-69, 159-163
  administration, route of, 69
  alpha vs. beta-heparin, 67
  anticoagulant activity, 66, 67
  antiheparins and, 68, 162
  antithrombin effect, 50
  blood levels of, 162
  chemistry, 66
  clearing factor, and, 159-164

metabolism, 67, 161
"oral heparin" and clearing factor,
  163
physiological importance, 162
serum protein and, 161
site of clearing action, 162
source of, 65
specificity in clearing, 161
therapy in coronary disease, 69, 163,
  179
thromboplastin generation, inhibition
  of, 67
toxicity, 69
Heparinase, 68
Heparinoids, 69, 161, 162
Hexadimethrene bromide, antiheparin,
  68
Hormones
  plasmin inactivation of, 72
  serum lipids and, 152-159
Hyaluronic acid, partially depolymerized, 164
Hydrochlorothiazide, 23, 28
Hypercholesteremia, 165
Hypercoagulability and thrombosis, 44
Hyperlipemia, 118
  clearing factor in, 162-164
  coronary disease and, 165
Hyperthyroidism, serum lipids in, 154
Hypochloremic alkalosis, diuretic induced, 26, 31
Hypokalemia
  chlorothiazide, due to, 26, 27
  digitalis toxicity, and, 32
Hyponatremia,
  diuretics and, 28, 31
  sodium depletion and, 32
  spirolactones and, 30
Hypopotassemia, *see* Hypokalemia
Hypothyroidism and
  atherosclerosis, 154
  serum lipids, 154-156

I

Indanedione
  coagulation factors and, 62
  derivatives of, 60, 62, 63
Infiltration theory of atherogenesis, 101,

104-106, 123, 128
Intestinal flora and cholesterol metabolism, 147, 175
Intimal thrombosis theory of atherogenesis, 106

L

Lathosterol, 139
Lathyrism, 102
Lecithin
  arterial wall, in the, 123
  atherosclerotic plaque, in the, 110
  thromboplastin generation and, 53
Linoleic and linolenic acids, 142
Lipid infiltration theory of atherogenesis, 101, 104, 123, 128
Lipid metabolism. *See also* Lipids of
  serum
  dietary protein and, 150
  thyroid effect on, 156
Lipid mobilizing factor, 163
Lipids of atherosclerotic plaque, 121-125
Lipids of serum, 112-129, 137-180. *See
  also* cholesterol and lipoproteins
  antibiotics, and, 177
  anxiety and, 150, 165
  blood coagulation and, 52
  brain extract, effect on, 169
  clinical significance of, 179
  dietary factors effecting, 137-151, 180
    calories, 150, 178
    carbohydrate, 146, 179
    cholesterol, 138
    cholic acid, 148
    fat, types of, 141-145, 180
    magnesium, 177
    protein, 147
  estrogen effects, 152-154
  exercise and, 150
  fibrin formation and, 52
  heparin effect on, 159-163, 179
  hormonal influence on, 152-159, 179
  obesity and, 151, 178
  para-amino-salicylic acid and, 177
  plaque formation and, 104-106, 121-129
  psychosomatic factors effecting, 165
  reduction of, 178-180
  β-sitosterol effect on, 169, 174

thyroid state and, 154-156
Lipoprotein lipase, *see* Clearing factor
Lipoproteins of atherosclerotic plaque, 125
Lipoproteins of serum, 105, 112-120
  alpha$_1$, 113, 117, 119, 152, 180
  alpha$_2$, low-density, 114-120, 122, 124, 125-129, 179
  amino acids, terminal, 117
  analytical ultracentrifuge for, 113, 114
  anxiety, effect on, 166
  beta$_1$, 113, 116-120, 126, 180
  beta, low-density, 114
  brain extract effect on, 170
  chemistry of, 115-120, 122
  cholesterol, ester and free, in, 118, 120, 122
  cholesterol:phospholipid ratio, 119, 120, 122
  chylomicra and, 115, 116, 179
  clearing factor and, 161
  dietary carbohydrate and, 146
  estrogens, effect on, 152
  "high density," *see* Alpha$_1$
  "low density," 113. *See also* Alpha$_2$ and Chylomicra
  nicotinic acid effect on, 176
  nomenclature, 113
  pre-beta, 115
  protein of, 112, 118
  selective deposition of, 123
  "S^f," 113, 114
  sitosterol and brain extract effects, 174
  standard S^f, 126
  thromboplastic complexes, as, 49
  thyroid effect on, 155-156
  triglycerides in, 112, 118, 122, 125
Low salt syndrome, 31
Lysokinases, 71

M
Mast cells
  heparin form, 65, 162
  serotonin secretion by, 55
  toluidine blue staining in, 66
Medial sclerosis, arterial, 101
MER-29, 177
Methionine

in prothrombin, 51
  dietary, and serum lipids, 147
Mortality rate, ix
  cardiovascular, reduction in, 79
Mortality rate, late after myocardial infarction
  anticoagulant therapy and, 76, 80
  dietary factors and, 146
  estrogen therapy and, 153
  heparin (clearing) effect on, 163
  sudden and unexplained, 77
Muscular thickening, arterial, 102
Myocardial infarction
  anticoagulant therapy in, 76-82
  coronary thrombosis and, 42, 76, **83**, 103
  experimental, 54
  extension of, 76
  mortality, early, 76
  recurrence rate reduced, 78, 153
  survival, late, 80, 153
  thromboembolic disease, and, 76, 81-**83**
Myocardial insufficiency, *see* Congestive heart failure
Myosin, 20
Myxedema, *see* Hypothyroidism
Myxomatous degeneration, arterial, 102

N
Neomycin
  hepatic coma, relief of, 28
  serum lipids, effect on, 177
Neutral fat, *see* Triglycerides, lipid
Nicotinic acid, 175

O
Obesity and serum lipids, 151, 178
Oleic acid, 142
Oxidative phosphorylation
  bishydroxycoumarin, and, 62
Oxycholesterol in atherosclerosis, 108

P
Para-amino-salicylic acid, 177
Periplocin, 9
Phenylindanedione, 63. *See also* Indanedione
Phosphatidylethanolamine
  platelet component, 49

thromboplastin formation, 53

Phosphatidylserin
anticoagulant action, 50
platelet component, 49
thromboplastin formation, 53

Phospholipids. *See also* individual phosphatides
arterial wall, of the, 123
atherosclerotic plaque, in the, 108, 124
blood coagulation, and, 49, 52, 53
hormonal effects on, 153, 159
lipoproteins, of the, 117-120, 122-123
thromboplastic, 49

Plasma thromboplastin antecedent, 47, 48, 50

Plasma thromboplastin component, *see* Factor IX

Plasmin, 70, 72-73

Plasminogen, 70-72

Platelets
clot retraction, due to, 56
deposition in thrombi, 42
factors of, 49, 55-56
hemostasis, and, 55-58
phospholipids of, 49
thromboplastin generation and, 48-50, 58

Potassium depletion, diuretic induced, 26, 27, 32

Proconvertin, *see* Factor VII

Protamine as antiheparin, 68, 162, 164

Protein
dietary effects of, 147-148
of plasma, digitoxin binding, 13

Prothrombin
conversion to thrombin, 46, 47, 50, 51
time, tests of, 50, 58, 65, 83
aspirin and, 64
d-thyroxine effect on, 158

R

Red cell lipid, 106, 108, 120-122, 128

Rice diet, 140, 146

S

Salicylic acid and prothrombin activity, 64

Saturated fatty acids, 140-145

Scillaren A and B, 8, 13

Serotonin
clot retraction, effect on, 52
hemostasis, effect in, 55

β-sitosterol and serum lipids, 139, 169, 171, 178

Sodium,
serum, *see* Hyponatremia
total body, 5, 29, 31, 32

Squill, 9, 13

Sphingomyelin *see* phospholipids
arterial wall, in the, 110, 123

Spirolactones, 22, 29, 30

Sterols. *See also* individual sterols
dietary, 138
fecal excretion of, 142, 144, 156, 172-175

Streptodornase, 72

Streptokinase, 72

Strophanthidin, acetyl-K-, 18

Strophanthin, 7

Strospeside, 10, 11

Stuart factor, 47, 48, 50, 56, 57

T

Therapy, *see under type* of therapy

Thevetin, 9

Thrombin
chemistry of, 51
conversion of prothrombin to, 46, 47, 50
fibrinogen conversion, role in, 51, 52, 56

Thromboembolism, 41, 76
atherosclerotic plaque, role in, 104

Thrombolysis, *see* Fibrinolysis

Thromboplastin
anti-thromboplastin factors and, 48
chemistry of, 49
generation of, 46, 48, 49, 56-57
plasma thromboplastin, active, 49
phospholipids in, 53
prothrombin, and, 50
tissue activation of, 49, 56

Thrombosis
atherosclerotic plaque, on the, 44, 103
early ambulation and, 43
fatty diet, with experimental, 54
incidence, 42, 76

pathogenesis of, 41-44
Thrombus, morphology of, 41
Thyroxine (D- and L-), effects of, 154-159
Toluidine blue, 66, 68
Triglycerides
  atherosclerotic plaque, of the, 124
  lipoprotein fractions, in the, 112
  serum level, effected by
    dietary carbohydrate and, 146
    dietary fat, and, 141
Triodothyronine and analogues, 156-157
Triparanol, 177

U

Ulcer, intimal, atherosclerotic, 104
Uricosuric effect of ethylbiscoumacetate, 63
Urginin, 9
Uroheparin, 68
Urokinase, 72

V

Vascular injury
  hemostasis and, 73, 74
  thrombosis and, 43, 44
Venous thrombosis, 42
Verodoxine glycoside, 10
Vitamin K derivatives
  and coagulation, 61
  competitive inhibition of, 62, 63
Vitamins, fat-soluble
  in lipoproteins of serum, 112

W

Warfarin, 64
Weight reduction diet, 178
  serum lipids and, 150

X

"X-protein," 112